Word Problems with Decimals, Proportions, and Percents

Paul R. Robbins and Sharon K. Hauge

J. WESTON

WALCH

PUBLISHER

Portland, Maine

User's Guide
to
Walch Reproducible Books

As part of our general effort to provide educational materials which are as practical and economical as possible, we have designated this publication a "reproducible book." The designation means that purchase of the book includes purchase of the right to limited reproduction of all pages on which this symbol appears:

Here is the basic Walch policy: We grant to individual purchasers of this book the right to make sufficient copies of reproducible pages for use by all students of a single teacher. This permission is limited to a single teacher, and does not apply to entire schools or school systems, so institutions purchasing the book should pass the permission on to a single teacher. Copying of the book or its parts for resale is prohibited.

Any questions regarding this policy or requests to purchase further reproduction rights should be addressed to:

Permissions Editor
J. Weston Walch, Publisher
321 Valley Street • P. O. Box 658
Portland, Maine 04104-0658

1   2   3   4   5   6   7   8   9   10

ISBN 0-8251-3752-7

CONTENTS

Chapter 4. **Multiplying with Decimals**

Chapter 5. **Dividing with Decimals**

Chapter 6. Decimal Problems That Require Using Two or More Operations

Chapter 7. Problems That Can Be Solved Using Proportions

Chapter 8. Introduction to Percents

Chapter 9. Word Problems That Deal with Increases and Decreases in Percents

Chapter 10. An Introduction to Calculating Interest

Chapter 11. Solving Word Problems with the Aid of a Hand-held Calculator

To the Teacher

This book of reproducible instructional text is designed to build student skills in several areas of major concern for most teachers: decimals, proportions, percents, and application of arithmetic skills through word problems.

Word Problems with Decimals, Proportions, and Percents parallels two other books by Paul R. Robbins and Sharon K. Hauge, *Word Problems with Fractions* and *Word Problems with Whole Numbers*. The books are not dependent on one another, but the current volume does, of necessity, assume student knowledge of fractions.

This series of books came into existence at the urging of J. Weston Walch, the founder of J. Weston Walch, Publisher. Mr. Walch recognized the need to provide texts for students that would not only teach the fundamentals of arithmetic, but would also show the students how to use these skills to solve word problems. He wanted texts that would help students learn these skills, while keeping the students engaged and interested.

The three word problems books emerged as a way of meeting this challenge. We were very pleased that the approach we used won acceptance by many classroom teachers as a tool for teaching problem-solving skills to their students. The books have remained staples in the Walch catalog since their original publication in 1982.

It is now time for a new edition of these texts. There are a number of reasons for this decision. One reason has to do with the prices mentioned in many of the word problems. To keep the word problems credible to the students, we had to use new, realistic prices. A second reason for the new edition is the explosion of new technologies that has entered the lives of young people. We wanted to include word problems that used these technologies as well as new information and ideas that have come from science. Thirdly, many students are now using hand-held calculators. We believe it is important to show students how to use calculators as tools in solving word problems.

With these needs in mind, we offer the second edition of *Word Problems with Decimals, Proportions, and Percent.*

Like the other two books in this series, *Word Problems with Decimals, Proportions, and Percents* is written at a level which almost all junior high and even younger students will handle comfortably. What's more, it can be used to advantage in consumer and general math classes at the high-school level. It presents a series of problems that young people will find not only interesting but worth trying to solve. And it presents the topics of its title with rare lucidity and conciseness.

We hope that you will continue to find *Word Problems with Decimals, Proportions, and Percents* useful in your classroom teaching. We welcome your comments.

To the Student

Word Problems with Decimals, Proportions, and Percents is the third volume in our series of worktexts that explain how to solve word problems in basic mathematics. In our earlier texts, we covered word problems that use whole numbers and fractions. In this text, we shall show you how to solve problems that use decimals, proportions, and percents.

In the earlier books, we explained in detail how to recognize which operations of arithmetic are needed to solve a particular problem: that is, whether you need to add, subtract, multiply or divide to find the correct answer. We did this by pointing out certain key words, phrases or ideas that are presented in the problem that act as signals or guides to help you decide what to do. In this text, we shall continue in this manner. However, we shall be briefer, since we have discussed some of these ideas before. If you have not worked with our earlier books, *Word Problems with Whole Numbers* and *Word Problems with Fractions*, we suggest that you look through them, as this will help you more fully understand the approach we will take in solving word problems in this workbook.

CHAPTER 1:
Introduction to Decimals

This chapter introduces students to decimal numbers, starting with essential and basic material, such as place value, and carries them through the history of decimal numbers, before culminating in a section on units of measurement. Each term is carefully introduced and defined, assuming no prior knowledge on the part of the students. Concepts are sequential, and procedures are indicated in a step-by-step process. All students should be quite comfortable with the material.

Chapter 1 covers terms and definitions, reading place value, contexts for the use of decimal numbers, and names and reasonable estimates for various units of measure in both the metric and English systems. Students are asked to practice reading numbers aloud. If it is feasible to have partners work on this activity, verbal work is enhanced. If not, you may ask students to *write* the answers in English. In the section marked *A Handy Rule . . .*, helpful hints are given to support student success.

Answers

Drill for Skill (I)

1. four tenths, **2.** thirty-six hundredths, **3.** seven hundredths, **4.** sixty-nine thousandths, **5.** nine hundred eight thousandths, **6.** seven thousand, three hundred, forty-five ten-thousandths.

Drill for Skill (II)

1. three and one tenth, **2.** three and fourteen hundredths, **3.** three and one hundred forty-one thousandths, **4.** three and one hundredth, **5.** three and ten hundredths, **6.** six thousand, three hundred, forty-eight and two hundred six thousandths.

Drill for Skill (III)

1. 3.6, **2.** 3.1, **3.** 3.4, **4.** 3.44, **5.** 7.0.

Drill for Skill (IV)

1. $\frac{1}{2}$, **2.** $\frac{19}{20}$, **3.** $\frac{751}{1000}$, **4.** $14\frac{9}{25}$, **5.** $9\frac{91}{100}$, **6.** $\frac{2}{5}$, **7.** $\frac{1}{4}$, **8.** $\frac{7}{8}$.

Name _____

Date _____

146
239
5708

Introduction to Decimals

We are now ready to start learning about decimals. Decimals are very much like fractions. In fact, you can sometimes change a decimal into a fraction that has exactly the same value as the decimal you started with. And even when you can't change it exactly, you can always come close.

The decimal point is one of the most important inventions in mathematics. The decimal point is a point (a dot) that is placed between the digits in a number *or* before the first digits in a number. The decimal point gives us information about the value of the number. To this day, we do not know the name of the person who invented the decimal point. Simon Stevin, who at one time was a bookkeeper in what is now Belgium—and who later became an engineer in the Norwegian army—is given credit for first explaining the basic ideas related to decimal numbers. He did his work around the year 1600 A.D.

Mr. Stevin did not use a point to write decimal numbers; rather, he wrote numbers inside circles to represent decimal numbers. In his notation, the number 35.84 would be represented as 35 ⓪ 8 ① 4 ②. Can you figure out what the numbers in the circles meant? In this notation, the numbers in the circles meant that 35 was to the left of the decimal point; 8 was one place to the right of the decimal point, and 4 was two places to the right of the decimal point.

The Basics of Decimals

A counting number with a decimal point in front of it is another way of showing what a fraction shows. It should be read the same way.

Some examples are shown below.

Examples	$.5 = \frac{5}{10}$	$.42 = \frac{42}{100}$	$.363 = \frac{363}{1000}$
	(five tenths)	(forty-two hundredths)	(three hundred sixty-three thousandths)

Below are the names of the place values for decimals up to billionths. (You will notice that to the right of the decimal point there are no units. You start with tenths!)

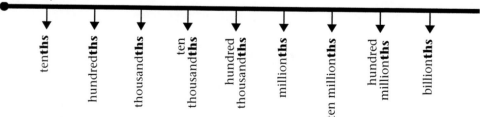

The names of all the place values end in **ths**.

         Word Problems with Decimals, Proportions, and Percents

A Handy Rule for Reading Decimals (A)

To read a number behind a decimal point, first read the number as though it were a counting number. Then say the name of the place value of the right-most digit.

.5 is read as "five tenths" (tenths)

.05 is read as "five hundredths" (hundredths)

.005 is read as "five thousandths" (thousandths)

.42 is read as "forty-two hundredths" (hundredths)

Drill for Skill (I)

Read the following decimals.

1. .4
2. .36
3. .07

4. .069
5. .908
6. .7345

Caution: Decimal values grow smaller as you move to the right in the place value chart.

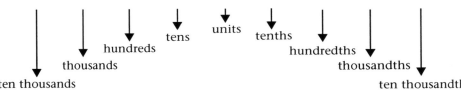

Hundredths are to the right of tenths on the place value chart. Therefore, one hundredth is smaller than one tenth.

.01 or $\frac{1}{100}$ is smaller than .1 or $\frac{1}{10}$

.02 or $\frac{2}{100}$ is smaller than .2 or $\frac{2}{10}$

.09 or $\frac{9}{100}$ is smaller than .9 or $\frac{9}{10}$, almost a whole.

Thousandths are to the right of hundreds on the place value chart; therefore, one thousandth is smaller than one hundredth.

.001 or $\frac{1}{1000}$ is smaller than .01 or $\frac{1}{100}$.

.002 or $\frac{2}{1000}$ is smaller than .02 or $\frac{2}{100}$.

.026 or $\frac{26}{1000}$ is smaller than .26 or $\frac{26}{100}$.

.099 or $\frac{99}{1000}$ is smaller than .99 or $\frac{99}{100}$.

(continued)

How small would .001 be? If you said $\frac{1}{1000}$, you are right. Imagine there are one thousand vitamin pills in a big bottle and you pick out one pill. That's $\frac{1}{1000}$ of the total or in decimal form .001.

If you keep adding zeros **after** the decimal point and **before** you have any other digit, the number gets smaller and smaller and smaller and smaller and smaller and . . . .

.0001 is $\frac{1}{10,000}$, and .0001 is smaller than .001.

.00001 is $\frac{1}{100,000}$, and .00001 is smaller than .0001.

Can you imagine a number like .000000001?

Scientists who deal with atomic particles use numbers like this. Sometimes they use even smaller numbers. In everyday life, however, you will seldom find a need to go beyond two decimal places, or hundredths.

DECIMALS AND WHOLE NUMBERS. Have you ever seen numbers where some of the digits come before the decimal point, and some of the digits come after the decimal point? Try to think of such a situation in everyday life. Well, how about this?

$$\$\$\$ \text{ dollars and cents } \cancel{c}\cancel{c}\cancel{c}$$

For example, $5.61 is five dollars and sixty-one cents. Think of five whole dollars, 6 dimes and 1 penny.

Now, think of the number 5.61 in the same way.

In the number 5.61

5 is a whole number as in $5. It is in the **units** place, just before the decimal point.

6 is after the decimal point in the **tenths** place.

1 is also after the decimal point in the **hundredths** place.

What does 5.61 mean? It is like you have 5 of something and a bit over, but you don't have 6. Imagine that you are taking a walk and you have gone between 5 and 6 kilometers, or you have a package that weighs between 5 and 6 pounds. 5.61 is for decimals what a mixed number is for fractions. It gives you a whole number and a fraction together. The decimal 5.61 is the same as the mixed number $5\frac{61}{100}$.

Name _____

Date _____

146
239
5708

Reproducible

Introduction to Decimals

A Handy Rule for Reading Decimals (B)

1. Numbers to the left of a decimal point represent whole numbers.
2. To read a number which has both digits to the left and to the right of the decimal point:
   (a) First read the whole number.
   (b) Say "and" when you reach the point.
   (c) Then read the part behind the decimal point.

Example	3.14 is read "Three and fourteen hundredths."

Note: This rule may be followed any time that you have a number to the left of the decimal point which is larger than 0. If you have ONLY 0 to the left of the decimal point, such as in the number 0.15, just ignore the 0 to the left of the decimal point, and read .15 as fifteen hundredths.

Drill for Skill (II)

Read   1. 3.1   4. 3.01
                2. 3.14   5. 3.10
                3. 3.141   6. 6,348.206

Exactness

You may have wondered, "What is the purpose of having whole numbers and decimals linked together? Why not just write the whole number and forget about the decimal?" The answer is that decimals give precision; they make numbers more accurate. Take dollars and cents again. You can say, "I have about 7 dollars," or you can say, "I have $7.44 (seven dollars and forty-four cents)." If you are going shopping, having the right amount of money to pay the bill is important. Having "about 7 dollars" might not be enough.

Or take baseball. You could say a pitcher has been giving up about 3 runs a game. Any baseball fan, however, would tell you—that other things being equal—a pitcher who is giving up 3.12 runs a game is pitching much better than one who is giving up 3.84 runs a game. So the decimals make it possible to better evaluate how the pitchers are doing.

So, decimals can give you a more accurate measure! The more digits you use after the decimal point, the more precise your measure is. While scientists may have need for great accuracy and need to use many digits after the decimal point, in many situations in everyday life, carrying out your answer to two decimal places is fine.

For many of the problems in this worktext, you will be told how many decimal places to write in your answer. If you have calculated an answer which has more than the required number of decimal places, you can always "round the answer off" to the required number of decimal places. We will now explain how to do this.

Rounding Off

Rounding off decimals is something like trimming. You've got more material than you need so you cut a little off. Imagine that you are a butcher and you have a meat cleaver and are chopping off the waste parts from the meat. Rounding off numbers in arithmetic is a little like chopping off the part of the number that doesn't add any useful information to the answer.

When you round off a decimal to two decimal places, you throw away all the digits after two decimal places. For example, the number 104.5610 rounded off to two decimal places becomes 104.56.

While that looks easy enough, rounding decimals can be a little more tricky. You may be wondering, when you lop off unneeded digits, should the **last** digit you keep stay the **same** as it is or should you **increase** the last digit you keep, to make up for what you threw away?

A Handy Rule for Rounding off Decimals

1. Find the digit that is in the final place you want to keep in your answer.

2. If the digit just to the right of the digit you found in Step 1 is **less than 5,** just lop off everything to the right of the digit in the final place you want to keep in your answer.

Example	Round 87.341364 to the nearest **hundredth**. Step 1. 4 is in the hundredths place. Step 2. 1 is less than 5. 87.341364 rounded to **hundredths** is 87.34, because the digit 1 which is just to the right of the place to which we are rounding off is LESS THAN 5. This means 87.341364 is closer to 87.34 than 87.35.

3. However, if the digit just to the right of the place to which you are rounding off **is 5 or greater than 5**, add 1 to the digit that is in the final place you want to keep and lop off the rest.

Example	Round 87.349462 to the nearest **hundredth**. Step 1. 4 is in the **hundredths** place. Step 2. 9 is greater than 5. 87.349462 rounded to **hundredths** is 87.35, because 9 is greater than 5. This means 87.349462 is closer to 87.35 than 87.34.

Drill for Skill (III)

Here are a few problems to practice.

1. Round off 3.56 to the nearest tenth. _____
2. Round off 3.09 to the nearest tenth. _____
3. Round off 3.436 to the nearest tenth. _____
4. Round off 3.436 to the nearest hundredth. _____
5. Round off 7.04 to the nearest tenth. _____

Changing Decimal Fractions into Fractions

Many decimals can be written as fractions whose denominators are numbers like 10, 100, 1000, etc. These decimals are called decimal fractions.

$$.5 = {}^5\!/_{10} = {}^1\!/_2 \qquad \text{AND} \qquad .333 = {}^{333}\!/_{1000}$$

0.5 and 0.333 are **decimal** fractions

${}^1\!/_2$ and ${}^{333}\!/_{1000}$ are **common** fractions

You may be wondering how to change (convert) decimal fractions into common fractions. This is easy. A decimal fraction can always be changed into a plain, old, ordinary common fraction, whose denominator is

10, 100, 1000, 10000, 100000, etc.

A Handy Rule for Changing a Decimal Fraction into a Common Fraction

1. Draw the fraction line.
2. Above the line, write the number which is behind the decimal point.
3. Below the line, write "1" followed by as many zeros as there are digits to the right of the decimal point (decimal places).

For example, look at .40.

(continued)

Example	Step 1. Write ——
	Step 2. Write 40
	Step 3. In .40 there are two digits to the right of the decimal point or "two decimal places," so write **100** in the bottom. $.40 = {}^{40}\!/_{100}$
	(Of course ${}^{40}\!/_{100}$ can be reduced to ${}^{4}\!/_{10}$ which can be reduced to ${}^{2}\!/_{5}$.)

Here are some more examples.

Examples	$.60 = {}^{60}\!/_{100}$ or ${}^{6}\!/_{10}$ or ${}^{3}\!/_{5}$
	$.75 = {}^{75}\!/_{100}$ or ${}^{3}\!/_{4}$
	$.79 = {}^{79}\!/_{100}$ (not further reducible)
	$2.10 = 2{}^{10}\!/_{100}$ or $2{}^{1}\!/_{10}$
	Write $.12\frac{1}{2}$ as a common fraction.
	You can read $.12\frac{1}{2}$ as "twelve and one-half hundredths." Let's follow our handy rule.
	In Step 1, we will write: —— .
	In Step 2, we will write: $\overline{12\frac{1}{2}}$.
	In Step 3, we will write: $\dfrac{12\frac{1}{2}}{100}$.
	This looks a little awkward, but you may recall from our fraction book that $\dfrac{12\frac{1}{2}}{100}$
	means $12\frac{1}{2} \div 100 = {}^{25}\!/_{2} \div {}^{100}\!/_{1} = {}^{25}\!/_{2} \times {}^{1}\!/_{100} = {}^{25}\!/_{200}$ or ${}^{1}\!/_{8}$.

Drill for Skill (IV)

Turn these decimal fractions into common fractions or mixed numbers.

1. .50 _____   5. 9.91 _____

2. .95 _____   6. .4 _____

3. .751 _____   7. .25 _____

4. 14.36 _____   8. $.87\frac{1}{2}$ _____

A Guide to Units of Measurement

For those of you who have grown up with units such as "inches," "pounds," and "gallons," here are some easy ways to understand the metric terms we will use.

1. **Liter.** The problem may say, "She poured out a half liter bottle of cola." What is a liter? A liter is just about the same size as a quart. When you see the word liter, think of a quart of milk.

2. **Meter.** The problem may say, "The board is two meters long." How long is a meter? Think of an overgrown yardstick. Imagine a yardstick about 39 inches long instead of 36 inches.

3. **Kilometer.** The problem may say, "The highway is 15 kilometers in length." The kilometer is a measure for longer distances. Picture in your mind riding in a car for half a mile. A kilometer is just a little more than that.

4. **Gram.** The problem may say, "She poured 5 grams of sulphur into a test tube." A gram is a measure of weight. How heavy is a gram? Not heavy at all. Think of something very light. Put a paper clip in your hand. A gram weighs something like that.

For those of you who have grown up using the metric system, an inch, a foot, a yard, and a mile are all measures of length. Think of

- an inch as roughly the distance across your eye
- a foot as about the length of a man's shoe
- a yard as a slightly shortened meter
- a mile as something less than two kilometers.

You should also keep in mind that

- a quart is just about the same as a liter.
- a gallon is just about as much as 4 liters.

A pound is a measure of weight. How much is a pound? Imagine a package of hamburger, big enough to make 3 or 4 good-sized patties. That meat would weigh about a pound.

9   *Word Problems with Decimals, Proportions, and Percents*

CHAPTER 2:
Adding with Decimals

This chapter introduces students to addition of decimals. The chapter starts with adding money, explaining and modeling the necessity of lining up the decimal points. After some practice with these straightforward calculations, students are introduced to word problems which require decimal addition to solve. *Key Words* are identified to assist students in figuring out the first problem set. In this manner, a mastery of problem solving with addition of decimals is built by starting with simple addition, an area of comfort for students, and stretching their understanding to the challenge of problem solving.

Chapter 2 uses specific instruction and *Key Words* to assist students in attaining mastery, Drill for Skill problems to assure that calculation skills are in hand, and Word Problems for Practice (I) to build confidence and mastery of interpretive problem solving.

Answers

"Put A Little Magic into Your Life"
a) It fits all criteria of a magic square, **b)** .66,
c) Yes, **d)** Answers vary.

Drill for Skill (V)

  1. 11.1, **2.** 64.52, **3.** 6.903, **4.** 5.56.

Word Problems for Practice (I)

  1. $4.10, **2.** 1.55 tons, **3.** 11.1 meters, **4.** 51.3 inches, **5.** 11 kilometers, **6.** 2.2 hours, **7.** 81.2 kilometers, **8.** $10.71, **9.** $460.97, **10.** 6.5 feet, **11.** $488.92, **12.** 7.8 miles, **13.** 47,256.3 miles, **14.** 21.41 minutes, **15.** 13.5 minutes.
China or Bust 1.84 meters.

Name _____

Date _____

Adding with Decimals

If you have ever added sums of money that included both dollars and cents, you'll find it easy to add decimals. For example, suppose you have to add two sums of money—let's say $36.10 and $12.60.

Example	How much is $36.10 plus $12.60?
Solution	You probably already know that when you add amounts of money, you must put these two numbers together neatly in columns with the decimal points exactly on top of each other and add, like this:

$$\begin{array}{r} \$36.10 \\ +\ \$12.60 \\ \hline \$48.70 \end{array}$$

Your answer is $48.70. That is 48 dollars and 70 cents.

Now if you add 36.10 + 12.60, you do exactly the same thing. The only thing missing is the dollar sign.

$$\begin{array}{r} 36.10 \\ +\ 12.60 \\ \hline 48.70 \end{array}$$

Your answer is 48 and 70 hundredths. It's very easy!

When you add decimal fractions, make sure to keep the decimal points in line, like this:

$$\begin{array}{r} 640.26 \\ 74.13 \\ 63.07 \\ +\ \ \ 4.30 \\ \hline \end{array}$$

If you don't, things will get more confused than you can imagine!

You will notice in the two examples below that the same "carrying rules" we used for adding whole numbers are used when we add decimal fractions.

Examples

$$\begin{array}{r} 11 \\ 59.64 \\ +\ 12.75 \\ \hline 72.39 \end{array} \qquad \begin{array}{r} 1 \\ 31.29 \\ +\ 5.48 \\ \hline 36.77 \end{array}$$

Name _____

Date _____

Drill for Skill (V)

Here are a few practice problems.

1.   4.7
    +   6.4

2.   62.09
       .45
  + 1.98

3.   .914
    1.265
     .654
  + 4.070

4. Here's a problem that looks a little different.
     3.1
   + 2.46

(Hint:	3.1 + 2.46	is the same as	3.10 + 2.46)

Filling zeros to the **right** of the last digit behind a decimal point does not change the value of the decimal.

For example, 3.1 has the same value as 3.10.

Why? $3.1 = 3\frac{1}{10}$, and $3.10 = 3\frac{10}{100} = 3\frac{1}{10}$.

        Word Problems with Decimals, Proportions, and Percents

Put a Little Magic into Your Life

Have you ever heard of Magic Squares?

There is an often-told story about an ancient Chinese emperor who found a tortoise on the bank of the Yellow River. The design on the tortoise shell was most interesting. It looked something like this.

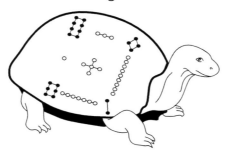

Look at the tortoise. If we put the numbers of dots we see on the tortoise's shell into rows and columns, we get a square that looks like this.

8	3	4
1	5	9
6	7	2

The sum of the numbers in each row (15) is the same as the sum of the numbers in each column (15) is the same as the sum of the numbers in each of the diagonals (15). Since all of these sums are the same, this square is called a "magic square," and its magic number is 15.

A magic square is a square made up of rows and columns of numbers, such that the sum of the numbers across any row, down any column or along any diagonal is the same. This sum is called the "magic number" of the square. Magic squares with very interesting symbols in them have appeared in African, Arabic, and Chinese mathematics.

Here is a square with some numbers in it which we made up.

(a) Why is this square magic?

(b) What is its magic number? _____

.33	0	.33
.22	.22	.22
.11	.44	.11

(c) Look back at our friend the tortoise. Can you get other magic squares from the picture of the tortoise by turning your book on its right side? on its left side? upside down? _____

(d) Can you make up a magic square of your own? Making up a magic square with your own numbers in it may be more tricky than you imagine.

13   *Word Problems with Decimals, Proportions, and Percents*

Solving Word Problems That Require Addition of Decimals

Now that you know how to add decimals, let's use your new skill to solve some word problems. Let's begin by asking, "What does addition mean?" Stated simply, addition means to put things together to come up with a total amount.

There are some key words and phrases in the English language that are signals for addition. These words include the word **total** and words that mean much the same thing as **total** such as **sum**, **all together**, and **in all**. Look for these words. Also, look for words that mean the same thing as **put together**, such as **join**, **combine**, and **accumulate**. When you see any of these key words or phrases in a problem, you can be pretty sure that the problem can be solved by addition.

Sometimes you will find that the **idea** of putting things together may occur in a problem without any key words or phrases, such as **total** or **all together**. When you see such a problem and you think you have to add, try putting one of these key words into the sentence. If the new sentence makes good sense and seems to say the same thing as the old sentence said, then you can feel more certain that the problem can be solved by addition.

Let's work two problems, one with a key phrase included, and the other without a key phrase included.

Example A	Lauren bought a used car to drive back and forth to her junior college. In November she put 1.3 liters of anti-freeze into the car. In December, the radiator hose broke, the anti-freeze leaked out, and she put in another 1.5 liters. In February, she had to put in another .5 liter of anti-freeze. How many liters of antifreeze did she put into her car all together that winter? _____
Solution	The problem asks you to put things together (amounts of anti-freeze) and come up with the total amount. The key phrase **all together** makes it even clearer that we must **add**.
	To solve the problem, take the numbers out of the sentences and put them in a neat column like this:

$$
\begin{array}{r}
1.3 \\
1.5 \\
+\ \ .5 \\
\hline
3.3
\end{array}
$$
Be sure to keep the columns straight. The decimal points are in line. Now Add.

The total is 3.3. Now put the word **liters** after your answer to make it complete. Remember you were asked to find the total amount of anti-freeze. Your **answer**, then, is **3.3 liters**.

(continued)

Example B	Al was having friends over later in the day to watch the football game on TV. He went to the supermarket to buy some things for his friends to eat. He bought a six-pack of soft drinks for $3.20 and a bag of potato chips for $.79. How much money did Al spend?
Solution	There is no key phrase for addition in the problem, but it's clear that you are being asked to put things together—the cost of the two items: the soft drinks and potato chips. Let's be sure, however, that we must add. First we'll insert one of our key phrases for addition at the end of the problem. Change the last sentence to "How much did Al spend **all together**?" The phrase fits perfectly and makes good sense.
	Having decided to add, let's take out the numbers, line up the decimal points, and . . .

$$\begin{array}{r} \$3.20 \\ +\quad.79 \\ \hline \$3.99 \end{array}$$

Your answer is $3.99.

Word Problems for Practice (I)

1. The ice cream parlor had been charging $3.70 for its jumbo banana split. Because of increased costs, the parlor raised the price by $.40. What was the new price for the jumbo banana split? _____

2. On an isolated island off the coast of South America, scientists were studying giant turtles. Two of the largest turtles the scientists found weighed .85 ton and .70 ton. What was the combined weight of these two turtles? _____

3. A tennis court for a singles match is 8.3 meters wide. When doubles matches are played, the court is widened by 2.8 meters. What is the width of a tennis court for a doubles match? _____

4. Carl was building a telescope. To make the telescope, he fastened two pieces of metal tubing together. The first piece was 36.5 inches long. The second piece was 14.8 inches long. How long would the telescope be when the metal tubes were joined? _____

5. To get to her class at the city university, Ellen had to take the subway for a distance of 6.7 kilometers, transfer to a bus that traveled 3.8 kilometers, and then walk for .5 kilometer. What was the total distance Ellen traveled from entering the subway station to school? _____

(continued)

6. The disc jockey at radio station WZZQ was getting his program ready for the afternoon Top Forty show. He took out enough musical recordings to play for 1.3 hours, figured his commercials would take .7 hour, and estimated that he would talk for .2 hour. How much time would this take in all? _____

7. During the winter, Lamar kept in training by riding an indoor bicycle. During one week, he rode the following distances: 9.5 kilometers, 13.4 kilometers, 12.6 kilometers, 8.7 kilometers,15.9 kilometers, 10 kilometers, and 11.1 kilometers. How many kilometers did Lamar ride that week?

_____

8. Juan went to the Hobby & Craft Shoppe to buy some materials. He bought red paint costing $4.20, glue costing $1.49, balsa wood costing $3.04 and sandpaper costing $1.98. How much money did Juan spend?

_____

9. Scott had an important job interview coming up. He decided to buy some new clothes to make a good impression. He bought a suit for $340.99, shoes for $79.99 and a tie for $39.99. How much did he pay in all?

_____

10. Henry made some stilts from narrow boards. He nailed some foot rests 1.2 feet from the bottom of the boards. So, when Henry went walking on the stilts, his feet were 1.2 feet above the ground. Henry is 5.3 feet tall without the stilts. What is the distance between the ground and the top of Henry's head when he is raised up on his stilts? _____

11. When Nelson got his first credit card, he went on a big buying spree, charging everything rather than paying cash. He got his car repaired on credit at a cost of $152.64, took his girlfriend out to a fancy restaurant at a cost of $36.28, and bought a plane ticket to Florida for $300. When Nelson gets his bill from the credit card company, how much will it be? _____

12. How would you like to take a walk over a 4.2 mile bridge that crosses a scenic bay? Once every year, the Chesapeake Bay Bridge in Maryland is closed to traffic, and thousands of people come from all around to walk over the Bay. Derek took the walk, felt good when he finished, then walked another 3.6 miles beyond the bridge. How many miles did he walk all together? _____

(continued)

13. Sara was on the way to the hospital to visit her grandmother who was recovering from surgery to replace her hip. In the directions Sara received, she was told that the hospital was 3.7 miles west of the high school she attended. When Sara reached the high school, just before she turned west, she noticed that the odometer on her car read 47,252.6 miles. What will the odometer read when she reaches the hospital? _____

14. One day, a patient who had a rarely seen tropical disease came into a doctor's office. Wanting to know more about the disease, the doctor ran a computer search of articles in the medical library. This computer search covered the previous five years and took 9.25 minutes to run. The doctor then ran a second computer search to look for some older articles. The second search took 12.16 minutes. The doctor was very pleased with the references he found. How much time did these computer searches take all together? _____

15. A televised debate was scheduled among the four candidates running for mayor of Middlebourg. The rules were that each candidate would make an opening statement of 2 minutes, a closing statement of 1.5 minutes, and would be given 10 minutes to answer questions from the audience. How much time woud each candidate have? _____

China or Bust

George got a globe for Christmas. The globe showed all the countries of the world just like a map. But the globe was neater, because you could spin it around and you could really see that the world was round. George had a younger brother named Harry. Harry spun the globe around so much that it made George dizzy.

"Why do you keep spinning the globe around, Harry?" George asked, rubbing his eyes.

"It's kind of like a game. I like to see if I can make it stop where China is. I like to look at China on the globe."

"Would you really like to see China?"

"Sure. That would really be neat."

"Well, just dig a hole in the back yard, keep digging—and sooner or later, you'll get there."

George didn't exactly mean that, but he would have said anything to stop Harry from spinning the globe around. In a few minutes, though, George heard the sound of a shovel digging into the ground. It was Harry on his way to China.

Well, everybody in the neighborhood got a big kick out of Harry and his project. The dirt was flying out of the hole and Harry was disappearing deeper into the ground. On the first day, he dug .75 meter; on the second, another .62 meter; on the third day, still another .32 meter. On the fourth day, Harry dug another .15 meter into the ground. Then he struck something.

"I hit something!" he called out. "I've reached China."

"Maybe it's the Great Wall of China," George said, amused. "Hit it hard and see."

Harry slammed the shovel into whatever it was, and a spout of water shot into the air. Poor Harry was drenched and had to be rescued from what was quickly becoming a mud hole. Soon, the whole yard was soaked with water. Harry had cracked an old, rotting water main.

Harry's father had to rush home from work and was very unhappy with what had happened. The man from the water department was even more unhappy. By the time the main was repaired, the yard had become a swimming pool.

When the mess was finally cleaned up, Harry's father calmed down and decided to take Harry to Chinese restaurant. After dinner, Harry opened up a fortune cookie that said, "Look up, not down!"

"Maybe you should fly to China, instead of digging," Harry's father laughed.

"That's just what I'll do some day," Harry replied. And you know, he'll probably do it. (He's a determined little fellow.)

How deep was the hole Harry dug before his attempt to reach China came to an end?_____

CHAPTER 3:
Subtracting with Decimals

This chapter introduces students to subtraction using decimals. It again starts with the subtraction of money, a familiar concept. More difficulty is introduced with larger numbers and students are asked to check their answers after completing a subtraction problem. After practicing these skills, students are introduced to using subtraction in word problems. *Key Words* are identified that require subtraction. Instruction is then given for solving subtraction problems that do not contain key words. A mastery of problem solving with subtraction of decimals is built by starting with simple subtraction skills—an area of comfort for students—and stretching their understanding to the challenge of problem solving in a variety of settings.

Chapter 3 uses vocabulary instruction and *Key Words* to assist students in attaining mastery, Drill for Skill problems to assure that calculation skills are in hand, and Word Problems for Practice to build confidence and mastery of interpretive problem solving.

Answers

Drill for Skill (VI)

1. 97.2, **2.** 91.561, **3.** 60.27, **4.** 59.84. **Magic Square II** Yes, it can be a magic square. Magic number is 1.65 and middle square should be .55.

Word Problems for Practice (II)

1. .4 seconds, **2.** $6.25, **3.** .5 minutes, **4.** $6.25, **5.** $6.62, **6.** $214.37, **7.** $544.50,

8. .004 inches, **9.** $3.35, **10.** 10 years, **11.** .058, **12.** 9.5 pounds, **13.** .05 points, **14.** 6.8 years, **15. a)** 1.9 million people, **b)** 14.1 million people. **"Welcome to the Information Age!" a)** .8 miles, **b)** 2.6 hours, **c)** 9.3 inches.

Subtracting with Decimals

Subtracting decimals is much like subtracting money. If you had $150.65 in your bank account and you had to write a check to pay a bill of $18.35, you would figure out how much you had left in the bank this way:

$$\begin{array}{r} \$150.65 \\ -\ \$\ 18.35 \\ \hline \$132.30 \end{array}$$

If you erase the dollar signs, you have the simple decimal fraction subtraction problem.

$$\begin{array}{r} 150.65 \\ -\ 18.35 \\ \hline 132.30 \end{array}$$

You subtract the same way. The answer is the same, only it's not dollars and cents. It's simply 132.30.

When you subtract numbers that have decimal points in them, keep the decimal points lined up (one on top of the other). If you have to borrow, just do it the same way that you borrow when you subtract whole numbers.

Some examples of subtracting with decimal fractions:

Examples				
$\begin{array}{r}36.12\\-\ 21.48\\\hline14.64\end{array}$	(borrowing)		$\begin{array}{r}894.294\\-\ \ \ 63.165\\\hline831.129\end{array}$	(subtracting with three digits to the right of the decimal point)
$\begin{array}{r}86.3\\-\ 2.1\\\hline84.2\end{array}$	(subtracting with one digit to the right of the decimal point)			

You can see that it doesn't matter how many digits are to the right of the decimal point. You subtract the same way.

20   *Word Problems with Decimals, Proportions, and Percents*

Drill for Skill (VI)

Here are a few practice problems for you to work and check. Any subtraction problem may be checked by adding the bottom number to your answer. If your work is correct, this total will be the top number.

1. 98.4   Check:
    – 1.2

2. 100.463   Check:
    –   8.902

3. 64.37 (Hint: Recall that   Check:
    – 4.1   4.1 is the same as 4.10.)

4. 64.   Check:
    – 4.1   (Hint: 64 is a whole
             number. It is to the left
             of the decimal point.   64 = 64.
             Now fill in the blank spots with zeros.   64 = 64.00)

Magic Square II

Here is another magic square problem for you. Can you make this square magic? (Hint: First figure out what the magic number of the square would have to be if the square were magic).

.22	.99	.44
.77		.33
.66	.11	.88

Solving Word Problems That Require Subtraction of Decimals

When a word problem asks you to look for a **difference** or **what remains**, you should set your mind to **subtract**.

Let us think about the idea of **what remains**. We could just as easily use the phrase **what is left**. Imagine, once again, that you are taking money out of the bank, and you have to figure out how much you have left in the bank. Or think about reading this book. How much have you read already, and how much remains to be read? Or, think about taking a trip in your car. You put gas into the car and then use some of it. How much gas is left in the tank?

As we have stated earlier, when you see either the idea of **difference** or **what remains** in a word problem, you should think subtraction. Now, some-

(continued)

times you will see these key words or phrases right in the problem. When this happens, you can be nearly certain that you will have to subtract.

Example	After a winter snowstorm, Mrs. Browning bought sleds for her two children. One sled was 4.5 feet long, the other sled was 3.2 feet long. What was the **difference** in the lengths of the two sleds? _____
Solution	In this problem, we must find the difference between the lengths of two sleds. We know that to find a difference we must subtract. Let's take out the numbers, 4.5 and 3.2, from the sentences. Place the larger above the smaller number, carefully lining up the decimal point. Then subtract: $\begin{array}{r} 4.5 \\ -\ 3.2 \\ \hline 1.3 \end{array}$ Our answer is 1.3 feet.

Finding Differences When There Are No Key Words

Sometimes, the key words and phrases we mentioned above are not present in the problem. However, if you read the problem carefully, you can still see that the problem is asking you to find a difference or what remains. When this happens, you subtract, just as if the key words were actually there.

Here are some phrases to look for.

How much larger is one thing than another?
How much faster is one thing than another?
How much taller is one thing than another?
How much heavier is one thing than another?

Example	Two boys were riding their bicycles to school. One boy was traveling at a speed of 15.5 kilometers per hour. The other boy was traveling at a speed of 11.2 kilometers per hour. How much faster was the first boy traveling than the second boy? _____
Solution	Let's work this problem. Take the numbers out of the sentences. Subtract $\begin{array}{l} 15.5\ \text{kilometers per hour} \\ -\ 11.2\ \text{kilometers per hour} \\ \hline 4.3\ \text{kilometers} \end{array}$ (speed of first boy) (speed of second boy) The answer is 4.3 kilometers per hour.

(continued)

Here is another idea to be on the lookout for—problems that ask you to find **increases** or **decreases** over time. When this happens, you are really being asked to find a difference, and you should subtract.

Often you will have to solve problems asking about **changes in prices**. The price may increase or it may be reduced, as in a sale. When you see such problems, you must find the difference between the old price and the new one.

A problem may ask you about **what remains** in front of you without actually using the words **what remains**. For example, a problem can ask you to find the unfinished part of a task or a trip. Another problem may ask you to find what is still owed or **what has not yet been used**.

Example	Mrs. Irby bought a 2-liter container of milk. After 3 days, her children had drunk 1.2 liters of the milk. How much of the milk was still in the container? _____
Solution	Let's solve this problem.
	"How much of the milk was still in the container?" is another way of asking, "**What remains**?". So we must subtract. Take out the numbers from the sentences.

$$\begin{array}{r} \text{Started with} \quad 2.0 \text{ liters} \\ - \quad \underline{\text{Used} \qquad\quad 1.2 \text{ liters}} \\ \text{What is left} \quad .8 \text{ liter} \end{array}$$

The answer is .8 liter.

Word Problems for Practice (II)

1. Claudette was trying out for the girls' track team. She found that she was best at running the 100-meter distance. When she first started running this race, her time was 13.7 seconds. After training, her time was 13.3 seconds. By how much did she improve her time for running this race? _____

2. Isaac took his car to the carwash. The usual price for washing a car was $7.50. However, Isaac had received a coupon in the mail which reduced the price by $1.25. How much did Isaac still have to pay for having his car washed? _____

3. Jerry and Florence were sailing sailboats across a small pond. Jerry's boat sailed across the pond in 3.7 minutes while Florence's took 4.2 minutes. What was the difference in the times it took the two sailboats to cross the pond? _____

4. Sandy wanted to buy a backpack to carry things back and forth to school. The backpack she wanted normally sold for $25. At a "back to school" sale, the item was advertised for $18.75. How much money would Sandy save, if she bought the backpack at the sale price? _____

(continued)

5. When the delivery man from the Pizza Palace came to Mrs. Kicci's house, he handed her a delicious pizza and a bill for $10.37. Mrs. Kicci looked in her purse and found $3.75. How much more money did she need to pay the delivery man? _____

6. When the brakes on Gary's car went bad, he took the car to Clem's Garage for repairs. The bill for repairing the brakes came to $294.37. Gary paid $80 and agreed to pay the rest in 30 days. How much money did Gary still owe?

    _____

7. A fiberglass canoe had been selling for $620. The price was reduced by $75.50. What was the new price of the canoe? _____

8. A machinist was making a very small piece of scientific equipment. When he measured the piece, he found it was .017 inch long. He had to reduce its length by .013 inch. How long would the piece be after it was shortened?

    _____

9. Sue went to the drugstore and bought a new loose-leaf notebook for school. The notebook cost $1.65. She gave the man waiting on her a $5 bill. How much change did she get back? _____

10. The planet Mars takes 1.9 of our years to complete its orbit around the sun. The planet Jupiter, which is farther away from the sun, takes 11.9 of our years to complete its orbit around the sun. How much longer does it take Jupiter to orbit the sun than it takes Mars to orbit the sun? _____

11. Al Williams was a switch-hitting outfielder for the City College baseball team. When he batted right-handed, he hit .323. When he batted left-handed, he batted .265. How much higher was his average when he batted right-handed than left-handed? _____

12. Mike looked at a chart which suggested what people should weigh at different heights. He found that for his height, he should weigh 115 pounds. He stepped on the scale. It read 124.5 pounds. How many pounds would Mike have to lose to reach the weight listed in the chart? _____

13. In the Olympic games, winners for gymnastics medals are decided by a group of judges. Sometimes the scores can be very close. In one season of summer games, the winner had a score of 79.175. The second-place finisher had a score of 79.125. What was the difference between the scores of the first- and second-place finishers? _____

14. Women tend to live longer than men. In a recent year, the life expectancy at birth for males was listed at 72.1 years. The figure for females was 78.9 years. How much longer was the life expectancy for females than males?

    _____

(continued)

15. Feeling a little crowded? Just wait. In 1995, the population of greater Tokyo was listed as 26.8 million people. It is expected that by the year 2015, the population will rise to 28.7 million people. (a) How large an increase would that be? _____ A much larger increase is expected in Lagos, in the west African country of Nigeria. In 1995, the population of the greater Lagos area was listed as 10.3 million. It is believed that by the year 2015, the population will rise to 24.4 million. (b) How large an increase would that be? _____

Welcome to the Information Age!

Every Sunday afternoon, Rebecca's grandfather would come for dinner. During the meal, Grandad would get into a friendly but spirited conversation with Rebecca's father about which generation had it harder—her grandad's or her father's. Grandad argued that he had to walk farther to school, had to work longer hours on the job—and besides, the snowstorms were worse. Dad argued that the snowstorms were just as bad these days, and he had to walk a long way to school himself. While the discussion usually ended pleasantly over a slice of apple pie, Rebecca decided to check out some of these things for herself.

One day, she rode on her bicycle the distance from Grandad's old home to where he went to school. It was a long way—2.4 miles. The next day, she did the same thing for her father's old route to school. It was 1.6 miles. Score one for Grandad! (a) How much farther did Rebecca's grandad walk to school than her father? _____

Next, Rebecca went to her computer and used the Internet to locate information about the average number of hours people worked per week between 1970 and 1990 when Grandad was working. On the average, people worked 37.1 hours. The nearest date she could find for her father's time was the year 1990. The average work week for 1990 was 34.5 hours. Score another one for Grandad! (b) What was the difference in the average work week between 1970 and 1990? _____

Next, Rebecca went to the library, where she found information on the total yearly snowfall for her city. She added up the snowfall for a three-year period when her grandfather was growing up, and found the total snowfall for those years to be 85.4 inches. She then added up the snowfall for the last three years, and found the total snowfall for those years to be 94.7 inches. Score this one for Dad! (c) How much more snow had fallen in the past three years than in the three years that Rebecca had chosen for her grandfather's time? _____

When Rebecca presented her findings at the next Sunday dinner, her grandad and her father had a good laugh, shook hands, congratulated Rebecca on her research skills, and then started arguing about whose generation had the better baseball players.

Multiplying with Decimals

This chapter introduces students to multiplication of decimals. Starting with a *Handy Rule* introduction to multiplying decimals, students are given the opportunity to practice with increasingly challenging numbers, considering place value in each problem. With their skills in hand, students are asked to solve word problems which require the multiplication of decimals. Multiplication problems are broken down into their component parts and students are shown how to approach them. Finally, students are introduced to word problems in which: a) total amounts are calculated, b) total lengths and weights are found, c) rate problems using the word "per" are considered, and d) area problems with squares and rectangles are addressed. All of these problems give students ample experience to build mastery and comfort with problem solving using multiplication of decimals. A mastery of problem solving with multiplication of decimal numbers is built by starting with simple multiplication skills, an area of comfort for students, and stretching their understanding to the challenge of problem solving in a variety of settings.

Chapter 4 uses several *Handy Rules* and a pictorial breakdown of a multiplication problem to assist students in attaining mastery, Drill for Skill problems to assure that calculation skills are in hand, and Word Problems for Practice in several areas where multiplication is applied to build confidence and mastery of interpretive problem solving.

Answers

Drill for Skill (VII)

1. 325.2, **2.** 328.32, **3.** 11.726, **4.** 44.772.

Word Problems for Practice (III)

1. $4.95, **2.** $2.37, **3.** $222.00, **4.** $23.75, **5.** $28.50, **6.** $5.00.

Word Problems for Practice (IV)

1. 2200 meters, **2.** 375 hours, **3.** 700 inches, **4. a)** 4.8 seconds, **b)** 33.6 seconds, **5.** 1238.5 years, **6. a)** 2.4 pounds, **b)** 50 pounds, **7.** 8.52 ounces, **8.** 17.28 megabytes.

Word Problems for Practice (V)

1. $47.50, **2.** $9.50, **3.** 34 hours, **4.** $13.75, **5.** 16.5 kilometers, **6.** $79,360.

Word Problems for Practice (VI)

1. .4 square meters, **2.** 97.75 square inches, **3.** 4.48 square meters, **4.** .000009 square inches.

Word Problems for Practice (VII)

1. 9 marbles, **2.** 48 calls, **3.** 250 kilometers, **4.** 650 hours, **5.** 112.7 kilometers, **6.** 6 pounds.

Name _____

Date _____

Multiplying with Decimals

Let's think first of multiplying with money. Imagine you had $1.20, (a dollar bill and two dimes) and you wanted to multiply that amount by twelve. You could find how much this was by multiplying like this:

$$\begin{array}{r} \$1.20 \\ \times\ 12 \\ \hline 2\,40 \\ 12\,0 \\ \hline 1440 \end{array}$$

The multiplying was easy, but where exactly do you put the decimal point? You know if you were multiplying a dollar and some change by twelve, it certainly isn't going to come out to $1440. That would be an easy way to get rich, if it worked that way, but it doesn't.

Let's try moving the decimal point one place to the left, like this: $144.0. No, one hundred and forty-four dollars is still too much for multiplying a dollar bill and some change by twelve.

Let's move the decimal point one more place to the left: $14.40. That sounds right. If we moved the decimal point still another place to the left, we would have $1.440, which is a dollar and some change—just about what you started with. So you can see that the correct answer is found by moving the decimal point two places left. 1440 becomes $14.40.

Now look again at the original problem.

You will remember that the **number of decimal places** in a number is the number of digits written to the right of the decimal point.

$$\begin{array}{r} \$1.20 \\ \times\ 12 \\ \hline \end{array}$$

You can see that the bottom number has no decimal places while the top number has two digits to the right of the decimal point.

A Handy Rule for Multiplying Decimals

To find out how many decimal places the answer to a multiplication problem with decimals should have, do this:

1. Count the number of decimal places in the top number you are multiplying. In this case ($1.20) there are 2.

2. Then count the number of decimal places in the bottom number you are multiplying. In this case (12) there are none.

3. Add the number of decimal places in the numbers being multiplied. 2 + 0 = 2. This will give you the number of decimal places in your answer . . . the number of places you must move left.

So, in this problem, you start with 1440 and move the decimal point two places left, to get 14.40.

(continued)

Name _____

Date _____

Some examples:

Examples	If you had	31.14 × .07	You would have four decimal places in your answer (two from both numbers).
	If you had	19.06 × 3.1	You would have three decimal places in your answer (two from the top number; one from the bottom number).
	If you had	836.946 × .067	You would have six decimal places in your answer (three from both numbers).
	If you had	649.1 × 63	You would have one decimal place in your answer (one from the top number only).

All right. Let's try a problem.

Example	961 × .18 7688 961 17,298	Solution	First multiply. The answer should have two decimal places. Your answer, then, is 172.98. That's almost one hundred seventy-three. That's a lot different from seventeen thousand two hundred ninety-eight! Is the decimal point important? You bet it is! Always look at your answer and ask yourself, "Does the answer I have make sense?"

 Drill for Skill (VII)

1. 81.3
   × 4

2. 912
   × .36

3. 4.51
   × 2.60

4. 364
   × .123

BE ALERT—THIS WORLD NEEDS MORE LERTS!

Once in a while, you might get a problem like this:

The multiplication is easy enough:

.13
× .46
78
52
598

.13
× .46

(continued)

28   *Word Problems with Decimals, Proportions, and Percents*

HOWEVER—

Your rule says there should be **4** decimal places in the answer. But 598 has only 3 digits. What do you do for the fourth place? How can you move **left** 4 places, when there are only 3 digits? Simply put a zero in front of 598. Then write the decimal point. Your answer is .0598.

Solving Word Problems That Require Multiplication of Decimals

There are three kinds of word problems that require you to multiply decimals. These problems are as follows:

Type I	Imagine you have a collection of items or things, and you can measure these items in various ways—possibly by cost, (for example, each item costs $1.50); or by weight (for example, each item weighs 3 pounds); or by height (for example, each item is 6 inches tall).
	If each of the items is the **same on any such measure**, you can find the total cost of all the items in the collection by multiplication. For example, if there are 10 items and each of these items weighs 3 pounds, you can find the number of pounds in all the items by multiplying 10 by 3 pounds (10×3).
Type II	When you are trying to find the area of a rectangle such as [.5" / 1"] or a square such as [.5" / .5"], **multiply the length by the width.**
Type III	When you have a (fractional) part of a whole thing or collection of things, you can find the actual number of things in the part you have. For example, imagine a friend has a collection of 60 comic books and you've read .5 of them. To find the number you've read, multiply the fractional part (.5) by the number in the whole collection (60).

Let us start with the first type of problem, as this is the type of multiplication problem you will probably see most often.

(continued)

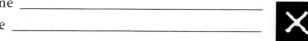
Type I: Finding the Total Amount

In such problems, something about each item will be in the **same** amount; you need to find the **total amount in all of the things**.

Example	Imagine that you are in the supermarket and you buy 6 cans of frozen orange juice. The cans cost $.59 each. How much would you pay in all? _____

A Handy Rule for Multiplication Word Problems (A)

To solve problems like this, multiply

the number of things	by	the amount of each thing	to get	the total amount of all the things.

Solution: With a problem involving money, like the total cost of the orange juice, you do it this way:

the number of cans	by	the cost of each can	to get	the total cost of all the cans.

That's 6 × $.59

$.59
× 6
─────
3.54   Your answer is $3.54.

Since you were looking for a total, you could also have found the answer by adding up the cost of each of the six cans, like this:

$ .59
.59
.59
.59
.59
.59
─────
$3.54

But when you have a bunch of things at the same price, it is much easier to multiply. **The idea is to multiply the number of things you have by the cost of the item.**

Word Problems for Practice (III)

1. Juan went on an errand for his mother to the post office to buy some stamps. He bought fifteen 33-cent stamps. How much did the stamps cost all together? _____

2. Rollie stopped at the bakery on his way home from school. There were delicious looking strawberry pastries in the window. He bought 3 of them at $.79 a piece. How much did the pastries cost in all? _____

3. One summer, Ruth found herself sneezing all the time and her eyes were watery. She went to a doctor who found she was allergic to some of the weeds that grew in the neighborhood. She had to get "allergy shots" once a month. If the shots cost $18.50 each, how much would the shots cost for a year? _____

4. Billy's mother had a hearing loss. When she wore a hearing aid, she could hear much better. If packs of batteries for the hearing aid cost $4.75 each, how much would 5 packs of batteries cost? _____

5. Mrs. Steiner treated six of the neighborhood children (three were her own kids) to a popular children's movie at the mall. They went to the early show. Tickets were $4.75. How much did Mrs. Steiner pay for the tickets? _____

6. Josh was a courier who delivered packages and letters around the city. Each of his stops was a short stop, so he used parking meters. At each stop he put a quarter into the meter. If during one week, he made 20 stops, how much did the meters cost him that week? _____

So far, our multiplication problems using decimals have all been about the cost of things. For example, cans of orange juice that cost $.59 each. But, as we have indicated, the idea of having a bunch of things where something is common to each of these things makes sense for many things besides money.

(continued)

Name _____

Date _____

✖

Example	Imagine 15 pieces of wood, each 2.4 meters long, which have been joined together to form one long piece of wood. What is the length of the long piece of wood? _____
Solution	You could add up the lengths for the 15 pieces of wood, of course, or you could simply multiply

the number of pieces of wood	by	the length (amount) of each piece
15		2.4

This gives us the following:

$$\begin{array}{r} 15 \\ \times\ 2.4 \\ \hline 60 \\ +\ 30 \\ \hline 36.0 \end{array}$$

The length of the long piece of wood is 36 meters.

Word Problems for Practice (IV)

1. Anita liked to jog around the track at the high school in the afternoon. The track was 400 meters long. If she ran around the track 5.5 times, how many meters would she have run? _____

2. One year, Ellen did volunteer work in the community hospital. She worked 7.5 hours each week for 50 weeks. How many hours did she work all together? _____

3. In the days of ancient Rome, people didn't use measures such as inches or meters. They used a measure called a "cubit." A cubit was believed to be 17.5 inches. Imagine an ancient Roman architect developing the plans for a house. If the structure was to be 40 cubits in length, how many inches would that be? _____

4. Reece did not notice that his watch was beginning to run ever-so-slightly fast. During every hour, the watch gained .2 of a second. (a) In 24 hours time, how many seconds did the watch gain? _____ (b) How many seconds did the watch gain in a week? _____

5. It takes a long time for the outer planets of our solar system to complete a journey around the sun. It takes the outermost planet Pluto 247.7 of our years to go around the sun. How many of our years would go by while Pluto made 5 complete trips around the sun? _____

(continued)

32   *Word Problems with Decimals, Proportions, and Percents*

Name _____

Date _____

Multiplying with Decimals

6. Dr. Mary McTavish is a biologist working on changing the characteristics of fruits and vegetables. She does this by cross-breeding plants and by using the new techniques of genetic engineering. One day, she looked at a tomato and weighed it. The tomato weighed 1.2 pounds. Dr. McTavish set a goal for herself to double the weight of the tomato. a) If she could do it, how much would the new tomato weigh? _____ b) What would happen if she doubled the size of a 25 pound watermelon? _____ A lot of good eating; but who would carry it?

7. During the year, Aaron's fish ate 6 bottles of flake food. If each bottle contained 1.42 ounces, how many ounces of flake food did his fish eat during the year? _____

8. The amount of data (bits of information) that can be stored on a computer diskette is measured in megabytes. Carla's mother bought a box of 12 diskettes. If 1.44 megabytes could be stored on one diskette, how many megabytes could be stored on the 12 diskettes that she bought?

_____

Type I Continued: "Per" Problems That Require Multiplication

Some word problems that require you to multiply contain the word **per**. When you see the word **per**, it does not automatically mean that you should multiply, for **per** is often used in division problems as well. So, you must look at word problems that contain the word **per** carefully before deciding what to do. This handy rule will help you.

A Handy Rule for "Per" and Multiplication

When a word problem contains the word **per** and you are **looking for a total, multiply**.

Example	Suppose that you are driving 60 kilometers per hour and you have driven 2.5 hours. How far have you driven? _____
Solution	The word **per** means "each." THINK: 60 kilometers **per** hour means 60 kilometers **each** hour. You want to know the **total** distance you have driven, so multiply:

number of hours driven	by	distance driven each hour	to get	total distance driven.
2.5 hours		60 kilometers per hour		150 kilometers

Word Problems for Practice (V)

1. Olivia set up a babysitting service that charged $4.75 per hour. What would be the charge for 10 hours? _____

2. Dave bought some buttercream chocolates for his grandmother. He bought 2.5 pounds of chocolates at a cost of $3.80 per pound. How much did Dave spend in all? (Round to two decimal places.) _____

3. The local university set up some new courses to teach students how to use computers. The students were each given 8.5 hours of time to use the university's big computer per semester. How much computer time would a student have over 4 semesters? _____

4. Sally's father liked to make wine as a hobby. He made the wine in his basement and gave it to his friends as holiday presents. If it cost him $.55 per liter to make the wine, how much would it cost him to make 25 liters of wine? _____

5. The whole Northlands area had been blanketed with snow. Chris got out her skis and went cross-country skiing with her boyfriend Mike. They moved at an average of 5.5 kilometers per hour. If they skied for 3 hours at this rate, how much distance would they cover? _____

6. The student activity fee at the Anderson Junior College was $12.40 per person. If the college had 6,400 students, how much money would the college make from this fee? _____

**Type II: Problems That Require Finding the Area
of a Rectangle or Square**

A Handy Rule for Multiplication Word Problems (B)

You can find the area of a rectangle by multiplying the length of the rectangle by the width of the rectangle.

width

length

The same thing is true for a square:

width

length

but, since all the sides of a square have the same length, you only have to multiply the length of a square by itself to find the area of a square.

(continued)

Example A	Imagine a nice new yellow rug. Like most rugs, it is in the shape of a **rectangle**. Let's make it 3.8 meters long and 3.1 meters wide. Find the area.
Solution	To find the area of this rug, multiply the length times the width. The area is 11.78 **square** meters.

$$\begin{array}{r} 3.8 \\ \times\, 3.1 \\ \hline 3\,8 \\ +\,114 \\ \hline 11.78 \end{array}$$

As you may remember from your study of whole numbers, the answer will be expressed as 11.78 **square** meters. If the length of the rectangle were 3.8 feet and the width 3.1 feet, the area would be 11.78 **square** feet. The word **square** must always be included in your answer when you are measuring area.

Example B	Imagine you are playing a game. You're seated at a table. It's one of those games like Monopoly™ where you shake the dice and move a piece around the board. This board is in the shape of a **square**. Each side is exactly 18.4 inches long. What is the area of the board? _____
Solution	To find the area of a square, simply multiply the length of the square by itself. In this case, the area of the game board would be 18.4 inches times 18.4 inches. That's:

$$\begin{array}{r} 18.4 \\ \times\, 18.4 \\ \hline 73\,6 \\ 1472 \\ +\,184 \\ \hline 338.56 \end{array}$$

The answer is 338.56 **square** inches.

Word Problems for Practice (VI)

1. There were some pretty wall posters on sale at the book store. The posters showed scenes from foreign countries. One poster which showed the snow-covered mountains of Switzerland measured .5 meter in width and .8 meter in length. What was the area of this poster? _____

2. Giselle had a stamp collection. A friend gave her a new album in which to display the stamps. The pages of the album measured 8.5 inches by 11.5 inches. How many square inches were there on a page? _____

(continued)

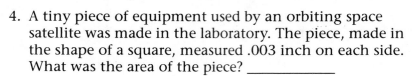

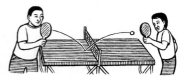

3. What is the area of a surface of a Ping-Pong table that is 2.8 meters long and 1.6 meters wide? _____

4. A tiny piece of equipment used by an orbiting space satellite was made in the laboratory. The piece, made in the shape of a square, measured .003 inch on each side. What was the area of the piece? _____

Type III: Problems That Give You a (Fractional) Part of a Whole or of a Collection of Things and Ask You to Find the Actual Number of Things in That (Fractional) Part

You may remember solving problems using fractions like this: Thirty people sang in the school choir. Two-thirds of the singers were girls. How many of the choir members were girls?

In problems such as this, you are given a fractional part of a whole thing or of a collection of things and you are asked to find the actual number of things in that part. Such problems are solved by multiplying.

A Handy Rule for Multiplication Word Problems (C)

Simply multiply:

| the fractional part you are given | by | the number in the whole group or collection | to get | the actual number of things in the part given. |

In the problem above, you were given that $\frac{2}{3}$ of the choir were girls; you want to find the number of girls in the choir. So, multiply:

$$\frac{2}{3} \times 30 \text{ to get } 20.$$

There were 20 girls in the choir.

(continued)

Example	Since a decimal fraction is a fraction, you can have the same kind of problem with a decimal fraction. You may be told that there are a certain number of things in a group —let's say there are 20 boats docked in the harbor—and .25 of these boats are sailboats. How many sailboats are there?_____
Solution	To answer the question, you take the fractional part given (in this case the decimal fraction .25) and multiply it by the total number in the collection (20).

$$
\begin{array}{r}
.25 \\
\times\ 20 \\
\hline
5.00
\end{array}
$$

Your answer is 5 boats.

Word Problems for Practice (VII)

1. Elmer had a collection of 90 marbles. He had acquired his collection in the following way. He bought .5 of the marbles, traded for .4 of the marbles, and won .1 of them in games with other players. How many of the marbles did he win in the games?_____

2. During the summer, Mary Jo helped at her father's office by answering the telephone. During one week, she answered 60 calls. She kept a list of the calls and found out that .8 of the calls were business calls and .2 were personal calls. How many business calls did she answer that week?

_____

3. If you were going to drive 500 kilometers, and during the first day you drove .5 of this distance, how many kilometers would you have driven the first day?_____

4. A space mission was designed so that the crew would spend 1000 hours orbiting the earth. When the crew had completed .65 of the mission, how many hours had they spent in space?_____

5. Sound waves travel through the air at a speed of about 1,127 kilometers per hour. How far would the sound of a beating drum travel in .1 of an hour?

_____

6. The blood in a person's body makes up .05 of the person's weight. If Micah weighs 120 pounds, how much does his blood weigh?_____

The Tallest Basketball Player in the World

"I want to win the championship," said the general manager of the Blue-Water Bounders to his scouts. "And I know just how to do it. Look everywhere, in every country in the world. Find me the tallest man alive and I'll make him into a basketball player."

"Everywhere?" the scouts asked.

"Everywhere," the general manager replied.

So, off they went—to Europe, South America, Africa, and Asia. One scout even went to the North Pole. The scout who went to Europe found a man who was 7.4 feet tall and a fine athlete. But the general manager said, "He's not big enough." Finally, the scout who went to Asia found a man who was 7.9 feet tall in his bare feet and topped 8.0 feet in basketball shoes. "Sign him up," the manager wired.

Urgi Urganivitch was the man's name, and he wasn't much of a basketball player. He couldn't dribble or shoot very well. But if he stood under the basket and you threw the ball high enough to him so no one else could reach it, he could always but the ball into the basket. His shot—which was only about 3 inches long—was deadly accurate. He never missed.

The sportswriters couldn't decide what to call the shot. It was not a hook shot, a jump shot, or even a lay-up. They finally decided to call it a "put-in."

One day, after Urgi had scored 146 points in a game, the other players in the league became fed up. They felt the "put-in" wasn't fair. So, they put their heads together to see if they could do something about the "put-in" shot. Finally, one player, who was very smart, said: "Hey, in professional basketball, they give 3 points for very long shots and 2 points for regular shots. Why don't we make them give only 1.5 points for the 'put-in'?"

Everybody thought this was a fine idea. The players met with the owners and demanded that the rules be changed or they would all go on strike. The owners did not want a strike, so they agreed. "Put-in" shots were reduced to 1.5 points. Even then, Urgi was the league's leading scorer. In one game, he scored 43 "put-in" shots. How many points would that be?_____

Dividing with Decimals

This chapter introduces students to division using decimals. Beginning with the vocabulary of division, students revisit familiar division concepts with single digit whole numbers. After this start, *A Handy Rule* discusses what to do when there is a decimal in the dividend, but not the divisor (Case 1). Once students are comfortable with this basic skill, problems are introduced in which the answers are repeating decimals. After practicing these skills, students are introduced to problems in which the divisor, but not the dividend, includes a decimal (Case 2). Ultimately, students also practice the third case, in which both the divisor and the dividend are decimals. After students have had sufficient practice with these three cases of division, they are asked to solve word problems in which division of decimals is required for solution. Starting with a section on "Division of a Whole into Equal Parts," followed by "Fitting Equal Parts into a Whole," and finally practicing with **Per** Problems That Require Division," students are given a description of a way to approach each type of word problem and then ample practice problems to increase their problem solving confidence.

Chapter 5 uses several *Handy Rules* and many examples of division problems to assist students in gaining understanding of the concept, Drill for Skill problems to assure that calculation skills are in hand, and Word Problems for Practice to build confidence and mastery of interpretive problem solving.

Answers

Drill for Skill (VIII)

  1. 32.09, **2.** 183.06.

Drill for Skill (IX)

  1. .02, **2.** .09, **3.** .002, **4.** .00003.

Drill for Skill (X)

  1. a) .2, **b)** .4, **c)** .75, **d)** .125, **e)** .875, **f)** .3, **2. a)** .67, **b)** .17, **c)** .06.

Drill for Skill (XI)

  1. 24.9, **2.** 188.9, **3.** 401.4., **4.** 9.2

Drill for Skill (XII)

  1. 46.0125, **2.** 20, **3.** 40.4, **4.** 20.3.

Word Problems for Practice (VIII)

  1. .6 meters, **2.** .7 minutes, **3.** $33.15, **4.** $99.98, **5.** 5.3 hours.

Word Problems for Practice (IX)

  1. 15 boxes, **2.** 82 albums, **3.** 400 laps, **4.** 10 boxes, **5.** 40 Covert engines.

Word Problems for Practice (X)

  1. 20 pages, **2.** $2.55, **3.** $60.18, **4.** 1.4 gallons, **5.** 1.5 tablets, **6.** 9 meters, **7.** $.40, **8.** 104,000 kilometers. **"The Princess with the Purple Hair"** 6 days.

Name _____

Date _____

Dividing with Decimals

Adding and subtracting decimals is quite simple. Multiplying decimal fractions is a little harder. Dividing with decimal fractions is a little harder still. But not all that hard. If you can divide whole numbers, you can divide decimal fractions. You do the same thing. The only thing you have to worry about is **where to put the decimal point**. Put it in the wrong place and you are out of luck.

Before we begin, let us briefly review the meaning of three very important words: **divisor**, **dividend**, and **quotient**.

When we divide:

1. The number we divide by is the **divisor**.

2. The number that is divided is the **dividend**.

3. Our answer is the **quotient**.

Example	
	$\quad\quad\quad\quad 5$ ⟵ Quotient
Divisor ⟶	$4\overline{)20}$ ⟵ Dividend

Now, there are three cases to learn about dividing with decimal fractions. Let us go to our mathematics bookshelf and pick up Case 1, "Decimal in the Dividend, But Not in the Divisor."

A Handy Rule for Dividing Decimals (A)

CASE 1: A Decimal in the Dividend, But Not in the Divisor.

This is where your divisor has no decimal point (like 65 in the example below), but your dividend has a decimal point (like 81.25 in the example below).

In this case, you divide as usual and put the decimal point in your answer **right above** the decimal point in your dividend.

Like so:

$$
\begin{array}{r}
1.25 \\
65\overline{)81.25} \\
65 \\
\hline
162 \\
130 \\
\hline
325 \\
325 \\
\hline
\end{array}
$$

(continued)

40   *Word Problems with Decimals, Proportions, and Percents*

Other examples:

| Examples | $\dfrac{4.2}{3\overline{)12.6}}$ | or | $\dfrac{140.16}{6\overline{)840.96}}$ |

Drill for Skill (VIII)

You can check each answer by multiplying the divisor by the answer. If your work is correct, the product will give you the dividend.

1. $3\overline{)96.27}$ Check:

2. $5\overline{)915.30}$ Check:

Division problems like the following example often cause students difficulty. Please look at this example carefully.

$14\overline{).28}$ Place the decimal point in the quotient.

$\overset{.}{14\overline{).28}}$ But notice that 14 will **not** go into 2, because it is larger than 2. To show this, you must write 0 in the quotient.

$\overset{.0}{14\overline{).28}}$ Now think 14 will go into 28 twice, so write 2 in the quotient.

$\overset{.02}{14\overline{).28}}$ Your answer is .02.
$\underline{28}$

Drill for Skill (IX)

Here are some problems like the above example for you to try. To be sure that each of your answers is correct, check it.

1. $15\overline{).30}$ Check:

2. $12\overline{)1.08}$ Check:

(continued)

Name _____

Date _____

÷

Reproducible

Dividing with Decimals

3. $32\overline{)\,.064}$ Check:

4. $49\overline{)\,.00147}$ Check:

You may have noticed that in each of the previous problems, the quotient came out exactly—there was no remainder. You might have asked, "What if the division does not come out exactly?" Well, there are two things that might happen. Let's take a look at each of them.

1. In the first case, the division finally comes out exactly if we add a zero or zeros at the end of the dividend. Here is an example:

$$
\begin{array}{r}
.25 \\
25\overline{)\,6.35} \\
5\,0 \\
\hline
1\,35 \\
1\,25 \\
\hline
10
\end{array}
$$

We have used all the digits in the dividend, but the division did not come out exactly. However, you will recall from our earlier work that 6.35 is the same as 6.350. So, write a zero at the end of 6.35, which will make the number 6.350. Continue to divide.

$$
\begin{array}{r}
.254 \\
25\overline{)\,6.350} \\
5\,0 \\
\hline
1\,35 \\
1\,25 \\
\hline
100 \\
100
\end{array}
$$

The division has ended.

2. In some problems, our division process never stops—regardless of how many zeros we write on the tail of the dividend. Here is an example of this:

$$
\begin{array}{r}
.3 \\
3\overline{)\,1.0}
\end{array}
\qquad
\begin{array}{r}
.33 \\
3\overline{)\,1.00} \\
9 \\
\hline
10 \\
9 \\
\hline
1
\end{array}
\qquad
\begin{array}{r}
.333 \\
3\overline{)\,1.000} \\
9 \\
\hline
10 \\
9 \\
\hline
10 \\
9 \\
\hline
1
\end{array}
$$

You can see that the division never stops!

(continued)

© 1982, 1999 J. Weston Walch, Publisher   42   *Word Problems with Decimals, Proportions, and Percents*

You might ask, "If the division never stops, how do I ever write an answer for problems like this?" Well, the answer you write down depends upon how many decimal places you want to include in your answer.

(a) If you want one decimal place in your answer, carry out the quotient to two decimal places. Then, follow the rules for rounding and round your answer off to one decimal place.

(b) If you want two decimal places in your answer (if you're dealing with dollars and cents, for instance), carry out the quotient to three decimal places. Then, round your answer off to two decimal places.

(c) If you want three decimal places in your answer (if you're dealing with batting averages, for instance), carry out the quotient to four decimal places. Then, round your answer off to three decimal places.

- The quotient in the above problem rounded to one decimal place is .3.
- The quotient in that same problem rounded to two decimal places is .33.

We could go on and on and on.

Before we bring down Case 2 from our bookshelf on dividing with decimals, this seems like a good place to answer a question we posed earlier.

Do you remember when we promised to show you how to change a common fraction into a decimal? Now you're ready for the explanation.

A Handy Rule for Changing a Common Fraction into a Decimal

To change a fraction into a decimal simply divide the bottom into the top.

Example

$\frac{1}{4} = 4\overline{)1}$

4 will not go into 1, but 1 = 1.0

$$\begin{array}{r} .2 \\ 4\overline{)1.0} \\ \underline{8} \\ 2 \end{array}$$

Add another 0 to the dividend:

$$\begin{array}{r} .25 \\ 4\overline{)1.00} \\ \underline{8} \\ 20 \\ \underline{20} \end{array}$$

So $\frac{1}{4}$ is the same as the decimal fraction .25.

This makes good sense, because $.25 = \frac{25}{100} = \frac{1}{4}$.

(continued)

Name _____

Date _____

| Example | .333 | In this situation, as we discussed earlier, the |

⅓ = 3 ⟌ 1.000
          9
         ___
          10
           9
         ___
          10
           9
         ___
           1

In this situation, as we discussed earlier, the division process does not stop—we get .3333333333333 . . . (The " . . ." is a sign which tells us that we could go on forever and ever and ever.) So ⅓ cannot be written as a decimal fraction, but it can be approximated (i.e., we can find an answer that is not exact, but close) by lots of decimal fractions, .3 or .33 or .333 or .3333 or . . ., depending upon how many decimal places we want to use.

Drill for Skill (X)

1. Change each of the following common fractions into a decimal fraction:

   (a) ⅕ = _____

   (b) ⅖ = _____

   (c) ¾ = _____

   (d) ⅛ = _____

   (e) ⅞ = _____

   (f) ³⁄₁₀ = _____

2. Change each of the following common fractions to a 2-place decimal fraction. Your answer will be only an approximation. (Carry out the division to **3** decimal places and follow the rules for rounding to round off your answer to two decimal places.)

   (a) ⅔ ~ _____   (b) ⅙ ~ _____   (c) ¹⁄₁₆ ~ _____

   The symbol ~ means **approximately**.

   Now let's haul down Case 2 from our bookshelf.

A Handy Rule for Dividing Decimals (B)

CASE 2: A Decimal in the Divisor, But Not in the Dividend.

This is where your divisor contains a decimal point, such as 2.5, but your dividend does not, such as 100.

In this case, (a) Forget about the decimal point in the divisor.
            (b) Add as many zeros to the dividend as there were decimal places in the divisor.
            (c) Now, divide.

(continued)

Example

$$2.5\overline{\smash{)}100}$$

The divisor 2.5 has one decimal place.

The dividend does not have a decimal point.

Follow the rule and write

$$
\begin{array}{r}
40 \\
25\overline{\smash{)}1000} \\
\underline{100} \\
0 \\
\underline{0}
\end{array}
$$

If your problem were $.25\overline{\smash{)}100}$, you would write $25\overline{\smash{)}10000}$.

If your problem were $.025\overline{\smash{)}100}$, you would write $025\overline{\smash{)}100000}$,

which is the same as $25\overline{\smash{)}100000}$.

Drill for Skill (XI)

In these problems, carry out the division two decimal places and round your answer to one decimal place.

1. $26.4\overline{\smash{)}658}$ _____

2. $3.14\overline{\smash{)}593}$ _____

3. $1.4\overline{\smash{)}562}$ _____

4. $2.6\overline{\smash{)}24}$ _____

NOTE: If the division does not come out exactly, your rounded-off answer multiplied by the divisor will not give the dividend exactly—EVEN IF ALL OF YOUR WORK IS CORRECT. However, if your work is correct, your rounded-off answer multiplied by the divisor should be close to the dividend.

Now, are we ready for Case 3.

A Handy Rule for Dividing Decimals (C)

CASE 3: Decimals in Both the Divisor and the Dividend.

Here's what you do.
$$.12\overline{\smash{)}10.80}$$

Count the number of decimal places in the divisor. Move the decimal point in both the divisor and the dividend to the RIGHT the number of places you counted.

(continued)

Example   In the example $.12\overline{)10.80}$, the divisor, .12, has 2 decimal places, so move the decimal point in both the divisor and dividend 2 places right. This gives you $12\overline{)1080.}$

$$12\overline{)\overset{90}{1080.}}$$

If you had $1.936\overline{)96.8}$, you would move your decimal points 3 places to the right in both divisor and dividend. To do this, you would have to add 2 zeros in the dividend to give you enough places to move the decimal. You would then have $1936\overline{)96800.}$

Drill for Skill (XII)

Try these. Carry out each division until the division process stops.

1. $.8\overline{)36.81}$ _____

2. $.42\overline{)8.4}$ _____

3. $2.4\overline{)96.96}$ _____

4. $1.3\overline{)26.39}$ _____

Solving Word Problems That Require Division of Decimals

We shall discuss several types of word problems that you can solve using your skills of dividing with decimals.

Type I

The first type of problem occurs when you are asked to divide something into equal parts. For example, imagine you have a board 3.6 meters long and are asked to divide it into 6 equal parts. How long would each part be?

Type II

The second type of problem asks you how many things of equal size will fit into a larger-sized space or container. For example, suppose you have a shelf that is 2.5 meters long and are asked how many .5-meter-long boxes will fit on the shelf.

Type III

The third type of problem deals with division problems which contain the word **per**. We will show you how to tell the difference between these problems and the problems using **per** that you solved earlier by multiplication.

Let's begin with the first type of problem mentioned.

(continued)

Type I: Division of a Whole into Equal Parts

To solve these problems, follow this simple rule.

A Handy Rule for Division Word Problems (A)

1. Put whatever it is you are dividing up on the **left** side of the division sign: ↑ ÷

2. Put the number of things you are dividing it up into on the right side of the division sign: ÷ ↑

3. Divide.

Example	Mrs. Mahoney received a check in the mail for $60.90. She decided to divide the money equally into two parts; one part to pay household expenses, the other to buy presents for her grandchildren. How much money would she have for the presents? _____
Solution	Ask: What is she dividing up? It's money, $60.90. Put this to the left of the division sign: 60.90 ÷
	Ask: How many parts is she dividing the money into? 2 parts. Put this to the right of the division sign: 60.90 ÷ 2
	Divide: $\dfrac{30.45}{2 \overline{)60.90}}$ The answer is $30.45.

Word Problems for Practice (VIII)

1. Wendell built a small greenhouse to put on the back porch of the house. The greenhouse was 1.8 meters long. He decided to divide the greenhouse into 3 equal parts in which to grow different types of plants. How long would each section be? _____

2. Four candidates were running for mayor. The public television station set up a program where the four candidates would debate each other. When the program came toward the end, there were 2.8 minutes left. The announcer then divided this remaining time equally for a closing statement by each candidate. How much time would each candidate have? _____

3. On New Year's Eve, the people living at 193 Perry Street threw a big party with many guests. The next day, they had to split up a bill for $132.60. One of the four hosts, Jim, offered to pay the sixty cents, but this did not go over too well. The four decided to split up the bill evenly. How much did each pay? _____

(continued)

4. Two college roommates decided to split equally the cost of getting on the Internet. They decided to use a local online service which charged $199.96 for a year. How much did each roommate have to pay? _____

5. At the mountain observatory, time using the powerful new telescope was limited. The program director announced that 15.9 hours of viewing time would soon be made available. Three staff astronomers asked for equal shares of this time. How many hours would each astronomer have for viewing? _____

Type II: Fitting Equal Parts into a Whole

 A Handy Rule for Division Problems (B) That Ask You to Find the Number of Things of Equal Size or Amount That Can Fit into a Larger Container

To solve problems like this, there is an easy rule:
Divide the larger thing by the smaller thing.

Example	The pet store had a number of hamsters which were kept in small cages. If the cages were each .3 meter wide, how many of the cages could fit into a 2.1-meter-wide space? _____
Solution	To solve problems like this, divide the larger thing by the smaller thing.

<u>Larger thing</u>   <u>Smaller thing</u>
2.1-meter space   .3-meter size for each cage

$2.1 \div .3$

$.3\overline{)2.1}$ (Move each decimal point one place to the right.)

$3\overline{)21}$ Your answer is 7 cages.

Word Problems for Practice (IX)

1. Mrs. Balzanowski has a 24-inch kitchen shelf where she stores different spices to liven up her cooking. The spices, such as garlic powder, clove, and oregano, are kept in small tin boxes, each 1.6 inches in length. How many of these boxes of spices can fit on the shelf? _____

2. Ashton keeps his collection of jazz albums recorded in the 1950's in a record cabinet he built himself. The cabinet has a space which is 16.4

(continued)

inches long to hold record albums. How many record albums, each measuring .2 of an inch, could fit into this space? _____

3. A track for auto racing was shaped like an oval. Each time a car went around the track, it covered 1.2 kilometers. How many trips would a car have to make around the track to cover a distance of 480 kilometers? _____

4. Wilhelm liked to garden. During the spring, he planted tomato seeds in small boxes and kept them inside the house on a ledge near a sunny window. The ledge was 36 inches long. If each box was 3.6 inches long, how many boxes would fit on the ledge? _____

5. One of the very early cars, the 1902 Covert, had an engine with only 6.5 horsepower. How many of those engines would you need to equal the power of a modern car with 260 horsepower? _____

Type III: "Per" Problems That Require Division

In our section on multiplication, we stated that the word **per** meant **each**. We solved problems like "You are driving 60 kilometers per hour and you have driven 2.5 hours. How far have you driven?" You can see that in the multiplication problem you were asked to find a **total** amount, in this case, the total distance traveled.

Per can also be used in division problems. When this happens, you are **not** asked to find a total amount. The total is given to you in the problem. Instead you may be asked to find **the amount per something**, like the number of kilometers per hour or the cost per person. This handy rule will help you.

A Handy Rule for "Per" and Division

When you are given a total amount and are asked to find the amount **for each** or **amount per something**, you use **division**.

Turn back to page 33 and compare the rule found there with this new rule.

Example	Let's try an example using kilometers per hour. Imagine you have been driving over the mountains. It's a twisting, turning road and you are not going very fast. In fact, after 1.5 hours, you've only gone a total of 16.5 kilometers. How many kilometers per hour have you been traveling? _____ You can see that this problem gives you the total distance traveled (16.5 kilometers). So you know you are not going to have to multiply. What you are asked to find is the number of kilometers traveled per hour. **To find an amount _per_ something, you must divide**.
Solution	You may ask, just what do I divide? Here is a handy way of solving division problems using "per."

A Handy Rule for Division Word Problems (C)

1. Take the basic information you are looking for out of the sentences.

    In this case, you are trying to find KILOMETERS TRAVELED PER HOUR.

2. Remember that what comes before **per** goes before the division sign ↑ ÷

    What comes after **per** goes after the division sign. ÷ ↑

3. Take out the numbers and put them where the words are. In the problem where you are driving the car over the mountain, put 16.5 before the division sign (the total number of kilometers traveled) and 1.5 after the division sign (the number of hours that have gone by).

4. Now, divide: $16.5 \div 1.5$

    $$1.5\overline{)16.5}$$

    Move your decimal point one place to the right in both divisor and dividend.

    ```
        11
    15) 165
        15
        ──
        15
        15
        ──
    ```

    Your answer is 11 kilometers per hour.

Word Problems for Practice (X)

1. Rebecca was doing some volunteer work recording books on tapes for persons who were blind or couldn't see well. During 2.25 hours, Rebecca recorded 45 pages from a new novel. How many pages was that per hour? _____

2. T-shirts were on sale at a price of $15.30 per half dozen. What was the cost per T-shirt? _____

3. The Mudtown softball team had nine players. If it cost $541.62 to provide uniforms and equipment for the players, how much would that be per person? _____

4. An earthquake destroyed many buildings in Capital City and damaged the reservoir. While the reservoir was being repaired, 3.5 million gallons of water had to be brought into the city each day. How much water would that be per person if 2.5 million people lived in Capital City? _____

5. Joe was a nurse. The doctor told him to give his patient .75 grams of medication. If the doctor also explained to Joe that there were .5 grams per tablet, how many tablets should Joe give his patient? _____

(continued)

6. Kay had a pet hermit crab named Hac. One day, Kay let Hac out of the fish-bowl where she kept him and let him wander around to get some exercise. During 3 minutes, Hac walked a distance of 2.7 meters. How many meters was that per minute?_____

7. A used bookstore was selling old wildlife and outdoor magazines for 3 for $1.20. How much money would that be per magazine?_____

8. In a science-fiction novel, a spaceship was hurtling toward the stars at a fantastic speed. It traveled 260,000 kilometers in only 2.5 seconds. How many kilometers per second was the spaceship traveling?_____

The Princess with the Purple Hair

Uncle Bill was a great storyteller. During the warm summer evenings, he would sit around with the neighborhood kids and tell them stories. One night, he said to the kids, "Tonight, I'm going to tell you a fairy tale called 'The Princess with the Purple Hair.' It's almost as famous as 'Snow White and the Five Dwarfs.'"

"Seven dwarfs," Junior Hawkins interrupted.

"What's one character more or less?" Uncle Bill said. "Quit nit-picking." He then began his story. "Well, the princess was of course very beautiful, and she had long blonde hair. Actually, I thought about calling her Goldilocks, but there already is such a character in a story about two bears."

"Three bears," Junior Hawkins interrupted.

"Three, you say? Okay. Well, the princess lived in a land where most of the women had blonde hair, and she decided she wanted to be different. She wanted to be noticed. So, she dyed her hair deep purple.

"When the people saw her purple hair, they were all amazed. People came from far and wide to see the pretty princess with the purple hair. Everything seemed just fine until one day, a giant who lived in a castle on a neighboring hill heard about her and decided to steal her away. The giant actually wasn't such a bad fellow until he read a book called *George and the Beanstalk*."

"*Jack and the Beanstalk*," interrupted Junior Hawkins for the third time.

Uncle Bill ignored the interruption and continued.

(continued)

The Princess with the Purple Hair
(continued)

"Well, when the giant read the book, he learned that giants were supposed to be mean creatures who do crummy things like stealing princesses. So, he figured he had to change his image. One night, he stole the princess away, took her to his castle, and then—to be even meaner—he told her that he was going to cut off her purple hair. 'Bit by bit,' he said, as that sounded even meaner. He got out his ruler and found the tresses of her hair measured 12.6 inches long. 'I'm going to cut off your purple hair 2.1 inches each day. And when I come to the end of these tresses, I'm going to turn you into a plum pudding.' Then he let out a feindish-sounding, 'Ho, Ho, Ho!' which nearly scared the poor princess to death.

"Well, as the days went by, the mean giant clipped off the princess's purple tresses piece by piece until the last one was gone. That very evening, the giant was supposed to return to carry out his threat to turn the princess into a plum pudding. But instead of the giant, a handsome young prince in shining armor walked into the room. He had come to rescue her. He beat up the giant and sent him running out of the castle as fast as his legs could carry him.

"Then, the prince took the princess into his arms. After he kissed her, he said, 'I'm sorry I got here too late to save your purple hair.'

"'That's all right,' she replied. 'I've found that having purple hair just gets you into trouble. Besides,' she added, while gazing into the prince's deep blue eyes, 'I think I shall go back to being a blonde. I've heard it said somewhere that blondes have more fun.'"

While the princess was figuring out how she could have more fun as a blonde, can you figure out how many days it took the giant to clip off all the princess's purple locks? _____

Decimal Problems That Require Using Two or More Operations

This chapter introduces students to problems which require a combination of steps and skills to solve. Two particular types of problems are discussed. Type I problems involve figuring out how much money you have. In these problems, students examine both income and spending to calculate financial standing. After several examples are displayed, students are asked to solve similar problems. Type II problems involve finding "averages." After an explanation of what is meant by average and an example, practice problems are provided. An historical discussion of the origin of averages is also included.

Chapter 6 closes with a 12-problem quiz, covering material introduced in Chapters 2–5. Students must identify and interpret which type of problem they are asked to solve and then perform the correct set of calculation skills.

Chapter 6 uses several *Handy Rules* and step-by-step procedures to ensure that students grasp the necessity of ordering multi-step tasks correctly. Word Problems for Practice are then used to build confidence and mastery of interpretive multi-step problem solving.

Answers

Word Problems for Practice (XI)

1. $113.79, **2.** No. George is $2.40 short, **3.** behind $0.40, **4.** $1,309.96, **5.** $24.82.

Word Problems for Practice (XII)

1. 6.13 meters, **2. a)** 15.5 pounds, **b)** Turkey 2, **3.** 200 miles, **4.** 3.67, **5.** .280, **6.** 2.9 hours.

Decimals: Final Quiz (XI)

1. 108.7 kilometers, **2.** .35 meters, **3.** 3.1 pounds, **4.** $66.64, **5.** .5 hours, **6.** $174, **7.** 3.11 million miles, **8.** 60 books, **9.** 85 points, **10.** 4.32 square meters, **11.** $42.75, **12.** $48.

Name _____

Date _____

Decimal Problems That Require Using Two or More Operations

In our other texts, we have described problems which have required you to use two different operations. Sometimes you had to add first, then subtract—or perhaps multiply first, then subtract. There are problems like this when you use decimals as well. The important thing to remember in approaching these problems is that you must go through several steps to solve the problems and you should think these steps out carefully before starting with your arithmetic. We will show you some examples of such problems using decimals.

Type I: Figuring Out How Much Money You Have

Most of us have money coming in—like pay checks, Christmas money, allowances or whatever—and we also have money going out—bills to pay, the grocer, the department store—you name it. Hopefully, you have more money coming in than going out.

Example A	What is your current financial situation? Maybe we shouldn't ask. Let's look at Bruce's situation instead. During one month, Bruce earned $25.60 delivering groceries to his neighbor up the street, and he got a $5 present from his grandmother. During that month Bruce spent $8 on movies, $9.40 on snacks and $4.50 buying some new socks. How well did Bruce do during June? Was he ahead or behind ("in the red," as they say)? _____
Solution	You can solve this problem in three steps:

(A) Add up all the money Bruce earned.
(B) Add up all the money Bruce spent.

Let's do it:

$25.60 $ 8.00
+ 5.00   9.40
$30.60   Total Received   + 4.50
                          $21.90   Total Spent

(C) Since the total Bruce received is greater than the total spent, Bruce is ahead. To find out how much he is ahead, subtract:

$ 30.60
– 21.90
$ 8.70   Net Gain

In June, Bruce was ahead by $8.70. Another way of saying this is, Bruce had a **net gain** of $8.70 during June.

(continued)

Example B | Not everyone is as careful with money as Bruce is. His cousin Dorsey is a big spender. During the same month of June, Dorsey earned $50.72 working part time at a gas station, and also received $15 from his father. However, Dorsey spent $35.20 on dates, $20.80 on snacks and bought new shoes costing $37.25. Let's see what Dorsey's financial situation was.

Solution

(A) Add up all the money Dorsey received:

$50.72
+ 15.00
$65.72   Total Received

(B) Add up all the money Dorsey spent:

$35.20
20.80
+ 37.25
$93.25   Total Spent

You can see that Dorsey spent more money than he took in. So we can't subtract the total spent from the total received to find out Dorsey's net gain for the month. All we can do is subtract the total received from the total spent to find out his net loss.

Total Spent $93.25

Total Received   − 65.72
$27.53   (**Net Loss**)

Dorsey was behind in June by the amount of $27.53.

A Handy Rule for Figuring Out Net Gains and Net Losses

1. Add up all the money received.
2. Add up all the money spent.
3. Subtract the smaller amount from the larger amount.

Word Problems for Practice (XI)

1. Mrs. Blanchard made 4 deposits in her bank during the month of November. These deposits were $120.63, $42.55, $130.00 and $22.81. During November she made two withdrawals from the bank. These withdrawals

(continued)

were $140.00 and $62.20. What was the net gain in her account during the month of November? _____

2. George went into the bike shop with three $20-bills in his wallet and a $.50-coin in his pocket. He wanted to buy the following items:

   A protective helmet costing $30.00

   A combination lock costing $17.95

   A tire pump costing $14.95

   Did George bring enough money to buy all these items? If not, how much was he short? _____

3. Al got into a penny poker game. When he started off, he wasn't doing very well. In the first three hands, he lost $.25, $.60 and $.35. Then he won $.80. Was he ahead or behind after the fourth hand, and by how much?

   _____

4. Over a four-week period, the Rent-a-Movie Shop had the following expenses:

   1st week $300.60
   2nd week $210.24
   3rd week $380.10
   4th week $400.00

   During these four weeks, the total amount of cash received was $2600.90. What was the net gain (profit) for the store during the four weeks?

   _____

5. The kids in the neighborhood put on a three-day carnival where they told fortunes, had games of chance and sold lemonade. During these three days, they received the following amounts of money: $14.20, $9.60 and $12.36. Their expenses for the three days were $3.10, $3.44 and $4.80. How much money did they make? _____

Type II: Finding Averages

These days, a lot of people jog for exercise. Dawnielle jogs every morning before going to school. One week, she jogged the following distances: 3.2 kilometers on Monday, 4.4 kilometers on Tuesday, 4.0 kilometers on Wednesday, 5.8 kilometers on Thursday, and on Friday when it rained, only .6 kilometer. One of Dawnielle's friends asked her, "How far do you jog each morning?" Dawnielle replied, "That changes from day to day. It depends on how much time I have, the weather, how I feel—things like that." Her friend then asked, "But can you tell me what you do typically; what do you **average**, for a morning's jog?"

(continued)

That was easy to do. Dawnielle knew that to find an average amount, she must first **add** the things she wished to average, then **divide** that sum by the number of things she added.

So she added the number of kilometers she ran each morning:

$$
\begin{array}{r}
3.2 \\
4.4 \\
4.0 \\
5.8 \\
\underline{.6} \\
18.0
\end{array}
$$

Then she divided this sum by the number of mornings she jogged, which was 5:

$$
5\overline{)18.0} = 3.6
$$

Dawnielle's answer was that she had jogged an average of 3.6 kilometers each morning during that week.

You can find other averages the same way.

A Handy Rule for Finding Averages

First add the things you wish to average, then divide this sum by the number of things you have added.

In our introduction to decimals, we stated that decimals are very useful in giving more precise answers to mathematics problems. Some very good examples of this occur in sports, where averages are figured to help show how well a player is performing. In computing these averages, you start out with whole numbers, do a division, and usually express the answer as a two- or three-place decimal to make the average more exact.

(continued)

Example | Let's take a baseball pitcher. In Chapter 1, we talked briefly about the number of runs a pitcher has given up. Let's say he's pitched 36 innings and during those innings has given up 13 runs that were not caused by a teammate's errors. Baseball teams keep a figure (**statistic**) called the **earned run average**, which is the number of runs the pitcher is charged with giving up **divided by** the number of innings pitched divided by 9.

So our pitcher would have an earned run average of 13 ÷ (36 ÷ 9) or 13 ÷ 4. Let's do the arithmetic.

$$\begin{array}{r} 3 \\ 4\overline{)13} \\ 12 \\ \hline 1 \end{array}$$

We could stop here and say his earned run average is 3 and something left over; but that would never do if you're a baseball manager. This has to be more exact. So the baseball team carries the division out two decimal places (or more, if necessary), like this:

$$\begin{array}{r} 3.25 \\ 4\overline{)13.00} \\ 12 \\ \hline 1\,0 \\ 8 \\ \hline 2\,0 \\ 2\,0 \\ \hline \end{array}$$

So our pitcher has an earned run average of 3.25.

Word Problems for Practice (XII)

1. Ronald was trying out for the school team doing the running broad jump. He made 3 practice jumps while the coaches watched him. The jumps were 6.1 meters, 5.8 meters and 6.5 meters. What was the average distance of his broad jumps? (Round to two decimal places.) _____

2. Caryn's mother sent her to the supermarket to buy a Christmas turkey. She told Caryn to buy a turkey of about "average weight." There were 5 turkeys for sale. The turkeys weighed the following amounts:

Turkey 1	20 pounds	Turkey 4	13.4 pounds
Turkey 2	16.5 pounds	Turkey 5	18.5 pounds
Turkey 3	9 pounds		

(a) What was the average weight of the turkeys? _____ (Round to one decimal place.) (b) Which turkey was closest to the average weight?

_____

(continued)

3. Back in the days of the Old West, mail was carried for a while by the Pony Express. The route was about 1900 miles long, running from Missouri to California. Each rider was supposed to ride for 75 miles and then give the mail to the next rider, something like a relay race. If a sack of mail took 9.5 days to travel from one end of the route to the other, what would be the average distance the mail traveled each day? _____

4. A baseball pitcher was charged with giving up 22 runs in 54 innings pitched. What was his earned run average? (Round to two decimal places.) _____

5. The shortstop for the Springville Women's Softball Team got 35 hits in 125 times at bat. What was her batting average? (Round your answer to three decimal places.) _____

6. As part of a class project, Don had to figure out how many hours a day he spent watching TV. Here is his record.

Sunday	— 4 hours	Thursday	— 2 hours
Monday	— 3 hours	Friday	— 3 hours
Tuesday	— 1 hour	Saturday	— 6 hours
Wednesday	— 1 hour		

What was his average TV viewing for a day? (Round to one decimal place.) _____

A Bit of History

We hear the word "average" all the time. Some of us may think of batting averages, for example. You may be interested in the history of how averages came to be used. Picture in your mind—sailing ships a long time ago. As the ships crossed the ocean, they carried goods such as spices from the East Indies. The ships tried to reduce their individual risks. One way they did this was to divide the value of the cargo that arrived safely at the port of destination among all the merchants who had shipped cargo on the ship. This way each merchant got an equal share of the profit.

Decimals: Final Quiz

We have now covered just about everything we planned to say about decimals. Before we move on to problems using proportions, let's make a final check to see how well you can now solve word problems using decimals. See how many of the problems you can solve correctly.

1. Holly and Francine were taking a bicycle tour. They traveled 30 days for a total of 3,260.6 kilometers. How many kilometers did they average per day? _____ (Round to one decimal place.)

2. There were two chimps standing next to one another in the zoo; the larger chimp, named Fritz, stood 1.60 meters tall. The smaller chimp, named Flossie, stood 1.25 meters tall. How much taller was Fritz than Flossie?

    _____

3. One summer evening, Jim's family got together for a seafood dinner. They bought .6 pound of scallops, 1.5 pounds of spiced shrimp and a 1-pound lobster. How many pounds of seafood did they buy all together? _____

4. Rhoda went on a shopping trip. She spent $36.24 for clothes, $18 for a birthday present for her father, and $12.40 for a compact disk. How much did she spend on this shopping trip? _____

5. Lori's father was a "no-nonsense" type of parent. When Lori went out on a Saturday night date, her father would blow his top if she didn't get back by 12:00. One night Lori and her boyfriend went to a movie starting at 8:00 which lasted for 3.5 hours. How much time did Lori have left before she had to get home? _____

6. The Shelton family visited Washington, D.C. during their summer vacation. While there, Mr. Shelton rented a car. The car rental was $43.50 per day. Mr. Shelton rented the car for 4 days. How much did he have to pay in all for this car rental?_____

7. When the earth travels around the sun, it sometimes gets a little closer than at other times. At its greatest distance, the earth is about 94.51 million miles from the sun. At its nearest distance, it is about 91.40 million miles from the sun. What is the difference in the distances between the earth and the sun when the earth is farthest from and nearest to the sun? _____

8. The Diamond Bookshop had copies of a book, *Sports Heroes of the 1990's,* displayed on a shelf 72 inches long. If each of these books was 1.2 inches thick, how many of them would fit snugly on the shelf? _____

(continued)

9. The history teacher gave the exam to end all exams. The exam lasted three days and had 200 questions. Any question answered correctly counted .5 point. If a student answered 170 questions correctly, how many points did she get? _____

10. What is the area of a stained glass window measuring 2.4 meters long and 1.8 meters wide? _____

11. Rudolph had $50.25 in his dresser drawer. He took $7.50 of the money with him in his wallet when he went shopping. He had bad luck and lost his wallet. How much money did he have left? _____

12. For her 18th birthday, Lisa received shares of stock in an oil company from her grandmother. The first month Lisa owned the stock, it gained $27.40 in value. The second month, the stock gained another $36.10 in value. The third month, the stock lost $15.50 in value. What was the net gain in the value of the stock over the three months? _____

Problems That Can Be Solved Using Proportions

This chapter introduces students to the concepts of ratio and proportion. Beginning with a pictorial description of what a ratio is, students are introduced to the language and symbolism of ratios. Drawing on everyday information, we discuss proportions and include some good visual examples. A procedure for solving problems with proportions is discussed, introducing students to the relationship between multiplication and division of fractions. Once students have mastered the calculation aspects of ratios and proportions, word problems are introduced. Several examples are presented in great detail, then students are asked to solve similar problems themselves.

Chapter 7 uses visual, careful and complete introduction of the concepts of ratios and proportions, including *Handy Rules* on both, and Drill for Skill on proportions. Word Problems for Practice then build on those skills to assist in building confidence and mastery of interpretive problem solving with ratios and proportions.

Answers

Drill for Skill (XIII)

  1. 2, **2.** 4, **3.** 3, **4.** .72.

Word Problems for Practice (XIII)

  1. 600 kilometers, **2.** 60 guppies, **3.** 6 defensemen, **4.** $40, **5.** 3.75 hours, **6.** 15 hot dogs, **7.** 20 inches, **8.** 18 inches, **9.** 1,000 officers, **10.** 9 minutes, **11.** 40 drops, **12.** 6 quarters. **"Estimating the Number of Fish in a Lake"** 9,375 fish.

Problems That Can Be Solved Using Proportions

Many word problems in mathematics can be solved by using proportions. To understand just what proportions are and how to recognize and to work problems which may be solved by proportions, it is important, first, to have a clear idea of what we mean by **ratio**. Ratio and proportion are closely related; they go together like a hot dog and mustard, or like two peas in a pod.

In our text on fractions, we presented an introduction to ratio. We will now review these ideas and then go on to show you how to solve word problems that may be solved with proportions.

The Meaning of Ratio

A _____

B _____

· Look at line segment A. Then look at line segment B. Which is longer? Line segment A, of course. How much longer is it?

You can see that it is 2 times (twice) as long. You can check this with a ruler. The ratio of line segment A to line segment B is 2 to 1 or $\frac{2}{1}$. Below you see line segment A again. Compare it to line segment C. If you measured each with a ruler, you would find that line segment A is 3 times as long as line segment C. The ratio of line A to C is 3 to 1 or $\frac{3}{1}$.

A _____

C _____

Ratios are used not only to compare lengths. They can be used to compare other quantities. Let's look at how they can be used to compare weights.

Harry weighs twice as much as Joe. The ratio of Harry's weight to Joe's is 2 to 1 or $\frac{2}{1}$.

Now let's see how ratios can be used to compare money. If Mary has $9 and Vanessa has $3, the ratio of Mary's money to Vanessa's is 9 to 3 or $\frac{9}{3}$ which may be reduced to $\frac{3}{1}$. $\frac{3}{1}$ has a value of 3. This, of course, means that Mary has three times as much money as Vanessa.

Finally, let's see how ratios can be used to compare ages.

(continued)

Name _____

Date _____

Eric is 2 years old; his mother is 20. The ratio of Eric's age to his mother's age is 2 to 20 or $^2/_{20}$ or $^1/_{10}$. This means that Eric is $^1/_{10}$ as old as his mother. However, as they grow order, the ratio of their ages will change. Since Eric's mother is 18 years older than Eric, when Eric is 10 years old, his mother will be 28. At that time, the ratio of Eric's age to his mother's age will be 10 to 28 or $^{10}/_{28}$ or $^5/_{14}$.

A Handy Rule for Ratios

A ratio is another name for a fraction. Ratios are used for comparing numbers.

$^3/_4$ is called "the ratio of 3 to 4." This ratio is sometimes written as 3:4. $^4/_3$ is called "the ratio of 4 to 3." This ratio may also be written as 4:3.

Proportions

Now that we have covered the meaning of ratio, let us move on to proportions. Did you ever build a model airplane? If you did, the model was like the real thing in the way it looked, only much smaller. In fact, some models of airplanes or trucks or trains are made to "scale." This means

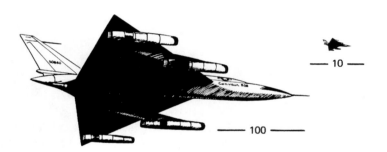

— 10 —

— 100 —

that the model is the same shape as the real thing, but it may be of a different size. If, for example, each part of the model is $^1/_{10}$ the size of the corresponding part of the original thing, then we have a model which has a scale of 1 to 10, and the "scale factor" is said to be $^1/_{10}$. In this case, the length of the model is $^1/_{10}$ the length of the real object; the height of the model is also $^1/_{10}$ the height of the real object; and the width of the model is also $^1/_{10}$ the width of the real object. In a word, the model is a miniature of the real thing.

In mathematics, we would say that the model is directly **proportional** to the real thing.

(continued)

A good illustration of proportion is a map. A map of anything should be in direct proportion to the real thing. If you saw a map of the United States that looked like this one, you would know that the map had been drawn incorrectly. Texas is way out of proportion.

TEXAS

Texans think big, but not that big!

When two things are directly proportional, every measurement of the first thing should be in the same ratio to the corresponding measurement of the second thing.

Example   If the map had been drawn correctly, the ratio

$$\frac{\text{Map length of Texas}}{\text{Actual length of Texas}}$$

would EQUAL the ratio

$$\frac{\text{Map length of Florida}}{\text{Actual length of Florida}}$$

The map was drawn incorrectly, because

$$\frac{\text{The map length of Texas}}{\text{Actual length of Texas}}$$

is LARGER than

$$\frac{\text{The map length of Florida}}{\text{Actual length of Florida}}$$

A Handy Rule for Proportions

A **proportion** is a statement that two ratios are equal. Since the word **ratio** is just another word for **fraction**, a proportion just says that two fractions must be equal.

Sometimes we are given two fractions and we have to find the missing part so that they form a proportion. For example, we might have $^?/_6 = ^1/_2$.

This is a very simple example because you know that $^3/_6 = ^1/_2$.

But, what if you were asked to find the missing part of this proportion?

(continued)

$?/10 = {}^{60}/20$

Maybe you can figure this out in your head, but most of us do better if we have a foolproof, can't-miss rule. We will soon show you such a how-to-do-it rule. This rule is based on the mathematical principle that **two fractions are equal if and only if the products are equal when we multiply diagonally across**. Let's explore this principle.

$3/6 = 1/2$ because $3 \times 2 = 6$ and $6 \times 1 = 6$.

$2/3$ is not equal to $3/4$ because 2×4 is not equal to 3×3.

We can use this principle to find the missing part in a proportion problem.

A Handy Rule for Solving Proportions

To find the missing part of a proportion, such as $?/10 = {}^{60}/20,$

1. Multiply each diagonal:

    $$20 \times ? \qquad 60 \times 10$$

2. Write the product of one diagonal equal to the product of the other diagonal:

    $$20 \times ? \ = \ 60 \times 10$$

    or $\qquad 20 \times ? \ = \ 600$

3. Divide by the number which was multiplied by the question mark (?):

    $$20 \overline{)600}$$ **The answer is 30.**

Drill for Skill (XIII)

Try these.

1. $?/3 = {}^{8}/12$

2. $3/? = {}^{9}/12$

3. $17/51 = 1/?$

4. $18/100 = ?/4$

         Word Problems with Decimals, Proportions, and Percents

Name _____

Date _____

Solving Word Problems with Proportions

Now let's try some word problems.

Example	Joe did not understand proportions. He was painting the walls of his bedroom and decided to thin the paint to make it go further. The manager at the paint store said he could thin this particular kind of paint by using 1 part water to 8 parts paint. However, Joe used 1.4 liters of water and only .6 liter of paint. The paint became so watery it ran right off his brush.
	If Joe had followed the directions how much water should he have used with .6 liter of paint? _____

A Handy Rule for Solving Word Problems with Proportions

1. Write down the two things that should be in direct proportion. In the above problem, these things are water and paint. So, write:

    WATER   PAINT

2. Make two fractions by using the words you wrote in Step 1. Then write = between them.

    $$\frac{\text{WATER}}{\text{PAINT}} = \frac{\text{WATER}}{\text{PAINT}}$$

    (Notice that these two fractions must match each other exactly. Since water is on top in the first fraction, water must be on top in the second fraction.)

3. Now, we must write numbers **in place** of the words in these two fractions. You can fill in the numbers for the **first fraction** from the information in the problem. The instructions call for 1 part water to 8 parts paint.

    WRITE: $\frac{1}{8}$ = $\frac{\text{WATER}}{\text{PAINT}}$

4. You can get the numbers for the **second fraction** from the question that is asked in the problem.

    The problem asks **how much water** should be used with **.6 liter paint**.

?	WATER
.6	PAINT

(continued)

The second fraction looks like this: $?/_{.6}$

5. Solve the proportion:

$1/_8 = ?/_{.6}$

$8 \times ? = 1 \times .6$ OR $8 \times ? = .6$

NOW DIVIDE:

$$\begin{array}{r} .075 \\ 8\overline{)\,.600} \\ \underline{56} \\ 40 \\ \underline{40} \end{array}$$

The answer is .075 liter of **water**.

Example	The high school started a club for students interested in modern dance. The club seemed to interest more girls than boys: there were 5 girls for every 3 boys that joined the club. There were 35 girls in the club. How many boys were there?

Solution

Step 1:   girls   boys

Step 2: $\dfrac{\text{Number of girls}}{\text{Number of boys}}$ = $\dfrac{\text{Number of girls}}{\text{Number of boys}}$

Step 3: $5/_3$ = $\dfrac{\text{Number of girls}}{\text{Number of boys}}$

Step 4: $5/_3 = {}^{35}/_?$

Step 5: $5 \times ? = 35 \times 3$ OR $5 \times ? = 105$

$$\begin{array}{r} 21 \\ 5\overline{)\,105} \\ \underline{10} \\ 5 \\ \underline{5} \end{array}$$ There are 21 boys in the club.

You may have noticed in the first problem the ? came in the top part of the fraction, and in the second problem, the ? was in the bottom part of the fraction. Always look for what is missing, what you have to find, and that is where you put the question mark.

Word Problems for Practice (XIII)

1. Alexa drove a motorcycle 200 kilometers in 3 hours. If she drove at this constant speed, how far could she travel in 9 hours? _____

2. George wanted to buy some guppies for his aquarium. The owner of the tropical fish store told him that 6 square inches of air surface would be needed for each 2 guppies in the tank. How many guppies could George put into his aquarium if the tank had 180 square inches of air surface? _____

3. Coach Goncalves of the Silver Blades hockey team liked to keep a 2 to 1 ratio of offensive players (centers and wings) to defensemen. If he had 12 offensive players in the squad, how many defensemen would he keep? _____

4. The department store was selling brightly colored terry cloth towels at 3 for $10. What would be the cost of 12 towels? _____

5. It takes Bernice 1.5 hours to type 6 pages. If she can continue at that rate, how long would it take her to type 15 pages? _____

6. The families in Arnie's neighborhood had an outdoor barbecue on a hot summer night. They cooked hamburgers and hot dogs on a charcoal fire. The people preferred the hamburgers to the hot dogs by a ratio of 4 to 3. If 20 hamburgers were eaten, how many hot dogs were eaten? _____

7. Chrissy took a great photograph of her boyfriend Hugo. The original snapshot was 3 inches tall and 5 inches wide. She had the picture enlarged so that it was 12 inches tall. How wide was the picture? _____

8. Esther sculpted a clay figure of a deer that was 2.5 inches high and 6 inches long. She decided to make a larger deer with the same proportions. The deer would be 7.5 inches high. How long would the deer be? _____

9. If an army needed 10 officers for every 500 enlisted men, how many officers would be needed if there were 50,000 enlisted men? _____

10. Robin lives on a street that runs into (intersects) a busy highway. To drive onto the highway, she has to wait for a stoplight that shines green most of the time for the highway. The ratio of the light's being green for the highway to its being green for Robin's street is 20 to 3. During a period of time, the light was green for the highway for a total of 60 minutes. During this period, how much time was the light green for Robin's street? _____

(continued)

11. Jed had an aquarium with very pretty tropical fish. One day, he noticed that some of the fish had developed spots on them. Jed talked to the manager of the store that sold him his aquarium. She suggested that he put some medicine into his aquarium. Jed was to use 2 drops of medicine for each gallon of water in his aquarium. If Jed had a 20-gallon aquarium, how many drops of the medicine should he put into his aquarium? _____

12. Kenny went with his mother to the clinic at the hospital where she would see a specialist for her heart problem. They parked the car at a meter and put 2 quarters into it. The meter gave them 40 minutes time. When they talked to the clinic nurse, they learned that the doctor was running late, and they should allow 2 hours for the clinic visit. If 2 quarters gave 40 minutes of parking time on the meter, how many quarters would be needed for 2 hours of parking time? _____ (**Hint:** First change 2 hours into minutes.)

Estimating the Number of Fish in a Lake

Can you imagine trying to count all the deer in a forest or all the fish in a lake? In such situations where the total number of individuals is very difficult to count, the total number may be estimated by using proportions.

Scientists interested in preserving wildlife wanted to estimate the number of fish in a lake. To make this estimate, they sailed into the lake and using nets, they caught a sample of 250 fish. The scientists then put tags on the fish they had caught and put the fish back into the lake. About one month later, the scientists went back to the lake. This time, they visited the same areas of the lake where they had previously caught the fish they had tagged. They lowered their nets into the water. This time they caught a total of 375 fish. Ten of these fish had tags on them.

The scientists then set up a proportion to estimate the number of fish in the lake. In setting up this proportion, they first compared the number of tagged fish caught on the second visit with the total number of fish caught on the second visit.

  10 tagged fish caught on second visit   375 total fish caught on second visit

You can see that $^{10}/_{375}$ of the fish they caught on the second visit were tagged.

The scientists then reasoned that this fraction should be close to the ratio of the tagged fish in the lake to the total number of fish in the lake. Since they had put 250 tagged fish into the lake on their first visit, and they did not know how many fish were in the lake at the time of their first visit, the scientists set up the proportion below to estimate the number of fish in the lake.

$$\frac{\text{fish tagged put into lake on first visit (250)}}{\text{total fish in lake on first visit \quad (?)}} = \frac{\text{tagged fish caught on second visit (10)}}{\text{total fish caught on second visit \quad (375)}}$$

Solve the proportion $^{250}/_? = {}^{10}/_{375}$ to find the scientists' estimate of the total number of fish in the lake.

Let Your Imagination Wander . . . .

We have described a number of situations in which proportions may be used—in scale drawings, in recipes, in calculating dosages of medicine, and in making estimates in environmental science. Can you think of any other situations in which proportions are used? Can you make up a word problem of your own that uses proportions? Can you solve it?

CHAPTER 8:

Introduction to Percents

This chapter introduces students to the important and pervasive concept of percents, after discussing the many places that students might encounter percents. The text describes the terminology and symbolism used in percent problems, including an historical reference. Next, skills are introduced, teaching students how to convert percents into decimals and decimals into percents. Once students have practiced these skills, word problems are introduced. A careful description, connecting percent problems to proportions, is given, and armed with these skills, students are asked to solve three types of word problems: 1) Finding the Number of Items That Make Up a Part of the Total, 2) Finding a Percent, and 3) Finding the Whole Amount. For each type of problem, a thorough description and examples are given, before students are asked to solve similar practice problems.

Chapter 8 uses *Handy Rules* and specific examples. The Word Problems for Practice in this section offer a wide variety of types of problems to ensure that students feel comfortable and confident with their interpretive percent problem solving.

Answers

Drill for Skill (XIV)

1. 31%, **2.** 215%, **3.** 200%, **4.** 50%, **5.** 370%, **6.** 37.5%.

Drill for Skill (XV)

1. .2, **2.** 2, **3.** .005, **4.** .00125, **5.** .875, **6.** .042, **7.** .35, **8.** .625.

Word Problems for Practice (XIV)

1. 48 words, **2.** $2.40, **3.** 20 words, **4.** 1,000 people, **5.** 18 questions, **6.** 9 terrible twisters, **7.** 25 cars, **8.** 100 students, **9.** 16 mice, **10.** 4,050 adults.

Word Problems for Practice (XV)

1. 5%, **2.** 80%, **3.** 75%, **4.** 12.5%, **5.** 25%, **6.** 80%, **7.** 15%, **8.** 10%, **9.** 20%, **10. a)** 80%, **b)** 30%.

Word Problems for Practice (XVI)

1. 60%, **2.** 25%, **3.** Jim: 50%, Florence: 30%, Mo: 20%. **"A Survey of the Graduating Class at Kennedy High School" a)** 48%, **b)** 20%, **c)** 12%, **d)** 8%, **e)** 2%, **f)** 10%.

Word Problems for Practice (XVII)

1. 20 fish, **2.** $1,900, **3.** 970 kilometers, **4.** 800 books, **5.** 25 hours, **6.** 5 kilometers, **7.** 60 kilometers, **8.** $10,000,000.

Introduction to Percents

Many everyday problems involving numbers are concerned with **percents**. When you listen to the news on TV, you hear the reporter use percents. "Inflation has held steady at 5 percent while unemployment has dropped to 3 percent of the labor force."

The sportscaster uses percents too. "Johnson is an excellent shooter. He takes high percentage shots near the basket. He's made 57 percent of his shots."

And so does the weather reporter. "There is a 30 percent chance of rain."

Sometimes, you hear a coach say that an athlete gives "100 percent effort." By that, he means the athlete tries as hard as he or she can. Can you imagine an athlete putting in 0 percent effort? How about a ballplayer, sitting on the bench, asleep?

So, 0 percent means nothing, while 100 percent means all. If you talk about people, 0 percent means nobody and 100 percent means everybody.

Most percents are, of course, somewhere between 0 and 100. The larger the percent, the more you are dealing with. For example, if we asked you and your fellow students, "Would you rather read this math book or go to a movie?" we would guess that only a small percent would choose the math book.

Percents are just like any other numbers. Ten percent is larger than 5 percent, 20 percent is larger than 10 percent, and 50 percent is larger than 49 percent.

Let's use politics as an example. Remember election nights? The newscaster says something like, "In the race for city council, Smudlump has 60 percent of the votes, while Jones has 40 percent." What does that mean? Well, for one thing, Smudlump looks like the winner. Another thing you notice is that the total adds up to 100 percent. If you take a total of anything and break it up into percents, the total will always add up to 100 percent.

> % is the symbol for percent

In an election, anything over 50% makes you a winner. Exactly 50% is a tie. One vote over 50% is a **majority**.

Percents are based on 100. If you had 100 people in a big room and found that 35 wore glasses, you could say that 35% of the people in that room wore glasses. If you counted the number of females in this same room and found that there were 57, you could say that 57% of the people were female.

A Little History About Percents

The word "percent" means the number of parts per hundred. Today, we write 57 percent as 57%. However, until the fifteenth century, we did not have the percent symbol. Before this time, it was common to see such phrases as "57 per hundred" or "57 P 100" or "57 cento." The percent symbol % is believed to have evolved from a symbol which appeared in an Italian manuscript written in 1425 and looked something like ſ.

A Handy Rule for Changing Percents into Fractions

Percent is the number of parts per hundred. 57% means 57 out of 100.

Percent is another way of expressing **a fraction with a denominator of 100**. Thus $57\% = {}^{57}/_{100}$. From this, we see that to change a % to a fraction, all we need to do is to drop the % sign, draw a fraction line, write the number above the fraction line, and write 100 below the fraction line.

A second way to change a percent into a fraction is to drop the % symbol and then multiply by $^1/_{100}$. If we use this method to change 57% into a fraction, we get $57 \times {}^1/_{100} = {}^{57}/_{100}$.

Examples	We will now look at some examples of changing percents into fractions. First, we will use The Handy Rule for Changing Percents into Fractions, and then we will use our other method which was described above.

$30\% = {}^{30}/_{100}$, which may be reduced to $^3/_{10}$.

$125\% = {}^{125}/_{100}$, which may be reduced to $^5/_4$.

$$62\tfrac{1}{2}\% = \frac{62\tfrac{1}{2}}{100}$$

Since a fraction actually shows a division, where the top is divided by the bottom, the difficult-looking fraction $\dfrac{62\tfrac{1}{2}}{100}$ may be simplified in the following way:

$\dfrac{62\tfrac{1}{2}}{100} = 62\tfrac{1}{2} \div 100 = {}^{125}/_2 \div {}^{100}/_1 = {}^{125}/_{200}$, which may be reduced to $^5/_8$.

Now, we will look at each of the above examples again. This time we will use our other method for changing each of these percents into fractions.

$30\% = 30 \times {}^1/_{100} = {}^{30}/_{100}$, which can be reduced to $^3/_{10}$.

$125\% = 125 \times {}^1/_{100} = {}^{125}/_{100}$, which is $1{}^{25}/_{100}$ or $1\tfrac{1}{4}$.

$62\tfrac{1}{2}\% = 62\tfrac{1}{2} \times {}^1/_{100} = {}^{125}/_2 \times {}^1/_{100} = {}^{125}/_{200}$, which can be reduced to $^5/_8$.

Which of the two methods for changing a percent into a fraction do you like better? When does it look like the Handy Rule would be easier to use than the second method? Can you think of situations where the second method is easier to use than the Handy Rule? What about changing $33\tfrac{1}{3}\%$ into a fraction?

$33\tfrac{1}{3}\% = 33\tfrac{1}{3} \times {}^1/_{100} = {}^{100}/_3 \times {}^1/_{100} = {}^{100}/_{300}$, which can be reduced to $^1/_3$. Isn't the second method for converting this percent into a fraction helpful?

(continued)

How do we turn these decimals into percents?

Question	Answer
What does .90 mean?	90%.
How about .65?	65%.
How about .10?	10%.
.05?	5%.
.01?	1%.

What we have just done works fine when you have exactly two decimal places, but sometimes you may have **more** than two decimal places, such as .639, or **less** than two decimal places, such as .2. What do you do then?

A Handy Rule for Changing Decimals into Percents

To change **any** decimal to a percent,

1. Move the decimal 2 places to the right.
2. Write the % sign.

Examples .27 = 27.% = 27%

.01 = 01.% = 1%

.175 = 17.5% (This example is very interesting, because it shows that percents can have decimal points!)

.5 = .50 (add a zero) = 50%

Change 4 to a percent.

In a whole number, the decimal point is understood to be after the number.

4 = **4.**

We move the decimal point 2 places right. Here, in order to move the decimal point 2 places right, we must first add two zeros. 4 = 4.00 = 400.% = 400%.

Drill for Skill (XIV)

Change each of the following into a percent.

1. .31 = _____   4. .5 = _____

2. 2.15 = _____   5. 3.7 = _____

3. 2 = _____   6. .375 = _____

Name _____

Date _____

Introduction to Percents

Changing Percents into Decimals

Changing a percent into a decimal is the opposite from changing a decimal into a percent.

 A Handy Rule for Changing Percents into Decimals

To change a percent to a decimal,

1. Move the decimal 2 places left.

2. Drop the % sign.

Examples	27% = .27
	6.5% = .065 (Here we could have moved the decimal point only one place left. That's why we had to write the zero.)
	300% = 3.00 = 3
	$5\frac{1}{2}\% = 5.5\%$ (because $\frac{1}{2} = 2\overline{)1.0}$)
	and 5.5% = .055

(division shown: $\begin{array}{r} .5 \\ 2\overline{)1.0} \\ \underline{1.0} \end{array}$)

 Drill for Skill (XV)

Write each of these percents as decimals.

1. 20% = _____

2. 200% = _____

3. .5% = _____

4. .125% = _____

5. $87\frac{1}{2}\%$ = _____

6. 4.2% = _____

7. 35% = _____

8. $62\frac{1}{2}\%$ = _____

Another method for changing percents into decimals is to first change the percent into a fraction, and then change the fraction into a decimal; for example,

Examples	$12\frac{1}{2}\% = 12\frac{1}{2} \times \frac{1}{100} = \frac{25}{2} \times \frac{1}{100} = \frac{25}{200}$, and 25 ÷ 200 = .125

       Word Problems with Decimals, Proportions, and Percents

Brief Review

We have now explained some of the things you need to know to work with percents. It is important to remember that a percent is another way of expressing a fraction with a denominator of 100. In various parts of this worktext, we have shown you how to change a fraction into a decimal fraction or decimal, and how to change this decimal into a percent. So, when you see a fraction or a decimal, you should know how to make a percent out of it. We have also shown you how to start with a percent and change this percent into a decimal. Because the explanations for making these changes are located in different places in this worktext, we thought it might be helpful to put these explanations together for you. So, we have drawn a road map to give you the whole picture of how to go from fractions to percents and back again. As our example, we are using the fraction ³⁄₅.

A Road Map Review of Some Handy Rules

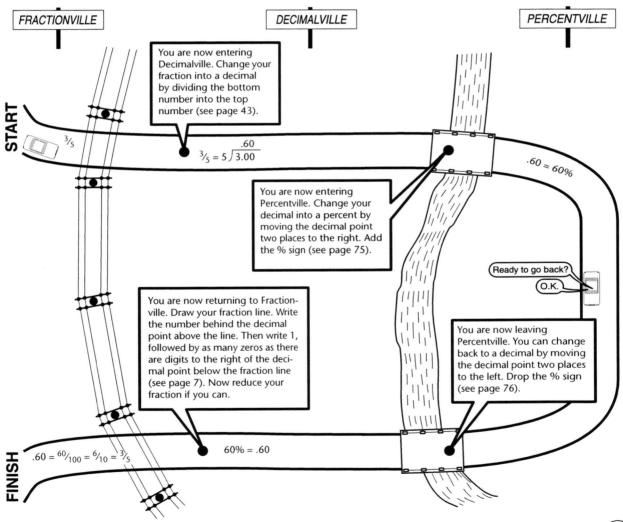

77 *Word Problems with Decimals, Proportions, and Percents*

A Table of Equivalent Fractions, Decimals, and Percents

We now know how to change fractions into decimals, and decimals into percents. Rather than do the work each time, it's sometimes better to have some of these values in a table, or better yet, in your head. When things are the same, like 50 cents and half a dollar, we call them **equivalents**. Here is a table of decimal and percent equivalents for some common fractions. Is this table worth memorizing? You bet!

Some Common Fractions	The Same (Equivalent) Value Expressed as a Decimal	The Same (Equivalent) Value Expressed as a Percent
$\frac{1}{2}$	.50	50%
$\frac{1}{5}$	.20	20%
$\frac{1}{4}$	.25	25%
$\frac{3}{4}$	.75	75%
$\frac{1}{8}$	.125	12.5% or $12\frac{1}{2}$%
$\frac{1}{3}$	$.33\frac{1}{3}$ or .333 . . .	$33\frac{1}{3}$%
$\frac{5}{8}$	.625	62.5% or $62\frac{1}{2}$%
$\frac{2}{3}$	$.66\frac{2}{3}$ or .666 . . .	$66\frac{2}{3}$%
$\frac{7}{8}$	.875	87.5% or $87\frac{1}{2}$%

Note: In the above table, we see that for some percents such as $33\frac{1}{3}$% or $66\frac{2}{3}$%, it is easier to work with their respective fractional equivalents $\frac{1}{3}$ and $\frac{2}{3}$, than it is to work with their decimal equivalents.

Math Buffs: You may wonder how we got $\frac{1}{3} = .333\frac{1}{3}$ or .333 . . . in the above table.

$$\text{Well, } \frac{1}{3} = 3 \overline{\smash)\begin{matrix} .33\frac{1}{3} \\ 1.0 \\ \underline{9} \\ 10 \\ \underline{9} \\ 1 \end{matrix}} \qquad \text{or } \frac{1}{3} = 3 \overline{\smash)\begin{matrix} .333 \ldots \text{ we keep getting 3's.} \\ 1.0 \\ \underline{9} \\ 10 \\ \underline{9} \\ 10 \\ \underline{9} \\ 1 \end{matrix}}$$

Name _____

Date _____

%

Introduction to Percents

Playing the Percents

It was a dramatic moment on the football field. The Iowa Flapjacks were playing the Eastern Nebraska Tornadoes. The Tornadoes had the ball on the Flapjacks' 14-yard line. It was fourth down with three yards to go for a first down. Coach Fiedler sent in his ace place kicker, Big Toe Zpowski, to attempt a field goal. The fans became restless. They wanted to gamble for a first down and a possible touchdown. "Go for it!" they shouted. "Ya bum!" others yelled. "Chicken!" was heard, followed by a chorus of booing.

Coach Fiedler sank into the bench as if trying to disappear from view. His job might be on the line. Big Toe approached to ball, hit it cleanly, and it sailed through the uprights. The kick proved to be the margin of victory as the Tornadoes won, 20 to 17.

Later in the locker room, a smiling Coach Fiedler talked to reporters.

"What made you go for the field goal, Coach?" asked Red Bonwedge, reporter for the *Gazette.*

"Just playing the percents, Red." He went on, "You see, Toe will make it 50 percent of the time from that distance. If we tried for the first down, we would make it maybe 20 percent of the time. Just playing the percents."

Word Problems That Require Using Percents

We will look at three basic types of word problems that use percents.

**Type I: Finding the Number of Items That Make Up
a Part of the Total Amount**

Example	There were 60 questions on the history exam. Justin got 75% of them right. How many questions did he get right?
Solution	As you study this problem, you can see that

YOU ARE GIVEN:

1. The total amount. (A total of 60 questions were on the exam.)
2. A percent (75) of that total amount.

YOU ARE ASKED TO FIND:

The actual number of items (questions) that make up a part (75%) of the total amount.

How do we solve such problems? Many percent problems can be solved by using proportions, so let us first look at this problem as a proportion problem.

You may notice that in this problem, two things are being compared.

$$\frac{\text{The number of questions Justin got right}}{\text{The total number of questions on the test}} \text{ IS COMPARED TO}$$

You will further notice that Justin answered 75% or $^{75}/_{100}$ of the total number of questions correctly. Therefore,

$$\frac{\text{The number of questions Justin got right}}{\text{The total number of questions on the test}} \text{ COMPARED TO} = {}^{75}/_{100}$$

This proportion is called a **percentage proportion**.

You can solve many percent problems as proportion problems by using the **percentage proportion**. Think of the percentage proportion as a kind of key that will unlock many percent problems.

THE PERCENTAGE PROPORTION SAYS

$$\frac{\text{Something compares with}}{\text{Something else}} \quad \text{the way} \quad \frac{\text{Some number compares with}}{100}$$

(continued)

A shorthand way of writing the percentage proportion is $^A/_B = {}^P/_{100}$.

Remember: "A over B equals P over 100."

Solving problems using the percentage proportion is a little like doing detective work—looking for the missing part. You can see that there are four things in the percentage proportion, A, B, P and 100. Now the numbers (values) you will use for A, B, and P will change from problem to problem, but 100 will stay the same in every problem we will give you. So you will only have to find the values for A, B, and P.

The word problem itself will provide you with two of these numbers. When you have put these two numbers into the percentage proportion, you can then solve the proportion and this will give you the third number—the missing number—the answer to your problem.

A Handy Rule for Solving Percent Problems

1. Write the **percentage proportion**: $^A/_B = {}^P/_{100}$.

2. Identify what the letters, A, B, and P stand for in the percentage proportion.

   To help you understand what the letters in the percentage proportion stand for, we will use the problem we stated earlier.

   There were 60 questions on the history exam. Justin got 75% of them right. How many questions did he get right? _____

   (a) **First**, find P. **P is the percent**. (In the above problem, P is 75.) Let's put 75 where P is in the percentage proportion.

   $$\frac{A}{B} = \frac{P}{100} \quad \text{becomes} \quad \frac{A}{B} = \frac{75}{100}$$

   (b) **Next**, find B. **B stands for the total or the whole thing**. B often comes right after the words "percent of" or "% of." (In our problem, B is 60, because there were a total of 60 questions on the **whole** test.)

   Now let's put 60 where B is in the percentage proportion.

   $$\frac{A}{B} = \frac{75}{100} \quad \text{becomes} \quad \frac{A}{60} = \frac{75}{100}$$

   (c) **Finally**, look for A. **A stands for what is being compared with the whole thing**. In our problem, the whole thing was 60. (There was a total of 60 questions on the exam.) The number of questions Justin got right is being compared with 60. Therefore, in our problem, A stands for the number of questions Justin got right. We don't know

(continued)

how many questions Justin got right. A is the question. Write a ? for A in the percentage proportion.

$$\frac{A}{60} = \frac{75}{100} \quad \text{becomes} \quad \frac{?}{60} = \frac{75}{100}$$

3. Do you remember how to solve a proportion? If not, we will review.

Our problem is $\frac{?}{60} = \frac{75}{100}$. Solve the proportion.

(a) Cross multiply: $\frac{?}{60} = \frac{75}{100}$

$$100 \times ? = 60 \times 75 \text{ or } 100 \times ? = 4500$$

(b) Then, divide by the number which was multiplied by ?. In our problem, we would divide by 100, so

$$100 \overline{)\begin{array}{c} 45 \\ 4500 \\ \underline{400} \\ 500 \\ \underline{500} \end{array}}$$

The value of A or the ? in this problem is 45. Justin answered 45 questions correctly.

In this problem, we used fairly large numbers in our fraction ($\frac{75}{100}$). Do you remember how to reduce fractions to lower terms? If you do, you know that you can reduce $\frac{75}{100}$ to $\frac{3}{4}$. If you do this, the proportion above will become $\frac{?}{60} = \frac{3}{4}$. You can see that doing the arithmetic now is much easier. When you solve percentage problems using the percentage proportion, look for chances to reduce your fractions before solving the proportion.

Math Buffs, How Are Your Recognition Sensors?

Using the percentage proportion is a surefire way to solve this type of problem. However, you can take a shortcut if your recognition sensors are sharp enough. Answering this problem is a lot like finding a fractional part of a whole. Suppose the above problem were worded:

There were 60 questions on the history exam. Justin got $\frac{75}{100}$ of them right. How many questions did he get right?

You know that to find the answer to this question, you multiply the fractional part by the whole amount. This would be $\frac{75}{100} \times 60$, or $\frac{3}{4} \times 60$ if you make things easier and reduce the fraction.

$$\frac{3}{4} \times 60 = \frac{180}{4} = 45$$

So you can solve these problems by first turning the percent into a fraction. You may solve the problem even more easily by turning the percent into a decimal. Let us reword the problem this way.

(continued)

There were 60 questions on the history exam. Justin got .75 of them right. How many questions did he get right?

Do you remember how to do this type of problem? If you don't, let's review for a moment. To get the answer, you multiply the fractional part (expressed this time as a decimal fraction) by the whole. That's

$.75 \times 60$ or

$$\begin{array}{r} .75 \\ \times\ 60 \\ \hline 45.00 \end{array}$$

or 45.

So, to use the short method, change the percent into a decimal—or fraction if you prefer—and multiply this decimal or fraction by the total.

Word Problems for Practice (XIV)

In the following list of problems, first **solve** each problem by using the **percentage proportion**. Then **check** your answer by using either a **decimal or fractional equivalent** to find the required fractional part of the whole.

1. Peter was working a crossword puzzle. There were 80 words to figure out in the puzzle. Peter managed to figure out 60% of the words. How many words did he solve? _____

2. Lucia and Tyler had lunch in a sidewalk café. It was a very nice place where they could watch all the people pass up and down the street. The bill came to $16.00. They left a 15% tip for the waiter. How much was the tip?

   _____

3. Dexter was learning to type. During a 5-minute practice period, he typed 250 words. However, he made errors in 8% of these words. In how many words were there errors? _____

4. The city council of Chesborough, a town of 50,000 people, was trying to decide whether to build a recreation center, complete with swimming pool and tennis courts. Councilor Morowicz, who was opposed to the project, said she thought only 2% of the townspeople would make use of the center. If she were right, how many people would that be? _____

5. Dana wanted to get an A in chemistry. To do this, her teacher said she had to answer 90% of the lab questions on the final exam correctly. If this final had 20 questions, how many of them must Dana answer correctly to get her A? _____

(continued)

6. The average number of tornadoes in the United States each year is 900. If one percent of these tornadoes have very high winds of 200 miles per hour, how many of these terrible twisters would be likely to occur in a year?

   _____

7. An antique car show was held near the county fairgrounds. 125 drivers brought their restored, polished, and pampered old cars to the show. If 20% of these 125 cars were built before 1930, how many of these were there?

   _____

8. There was a bad outbreak of flu at Walt Whitman Middle School. Forty percent of the 250 students in the seventh grade came down with the flu. How many of these seventh-grade students got the flu? _____

9. A new anti-cancer drug was tried out on 200 mice. If 8% of these mice had some bad reactions to the drug, how many mice was that? _____

10. After she had developed an ear infection while swimming, Beth went to the ear doctor. While she was in his office, she read a pamphlet about snoring. It said that 45% of adults snore. A recent census showed that there are 9,000 adults in her town, Grandview. Based on the pamphlet Beth read, how many adult snorers would you expect to find in Grandview? _____ (When Beth read further into the pamphlet, she learned that people snore more when sleeping on their backs than when they sleep on their sides. The pamphlet suggested that a snorer could sew a tennis ball into the back of his pajamas to nudge him from sleeping on his back into sleeping on his side. How does this idea grab you?)

Type II: **Finding a Percent**

Example	Here is an example of a second type of word problems that use percents. One summer, Dottie borrowed her uncle's movie camera. She wanted to make a short film about life in her neighborhood. She figured it would cost her $200 to make the film. She had $180. What **percent** of the total amount of money needed to make the film did Dottie have?
Solution	YOU ARE GIVEN: the total amount of money needed to make the film and the amount of money Dottie had. YOU ARE ASKED TO FIND: a percent (the percent of the money needed that Dottie had).

Let's solve this problem by using the percentage proportion.

1. Write A/B = P/100

2. (a) Once again, P stands for Percent.

> We don't know P. This is what we must find—the missing part.
>
> P is a ?. Let's put the ? into the percentage proportion where P is.
>
> $^A/_B = {}^P/_{100}$ becomes $^A/_B = {}^?/_{100}$

   (b) As before, B stands for the total. The total in this problem is $200, the total amount of money needed to make the film. Let's put 200 into the percentage proportion where B is.

   $^A/_B = {}^?/_{100}$ becomes $^A/_{200} = {}^?/_{100}$

   (c) Once again, A stands for what is being compared to the total. The money Dottie has ($180) is being compared to the total amount of money needed. So A = $180.
   $^A/_B = {}^?/_{100}$ becomes $^{180}/_{200} = {}^?/_{100}$

3. When we cross multiply, we get

$$200 \times ? = \begin{array}{r} 180 \\ \times\ 100 \\ \hline 18000 \end{array}$$

DIVIDE

$$\begin{array}{r} 90 \\ 200\overline{)18000} \\ \underline{1800} \end{array}$$

The answer 90 stands for the percent. Therefore the answer is 90%. Dottie had 90% of the money she needed.

(continued)

Look back at the problem again. You could have made the numbers much easier to work with by reducing $^{180}\!/_{200}$. For example, you can see that 10 goes into each number exactly, so $^{180}\!/_{200} = {}^{18}\!/_{20}$. And 2 will go into both 18 and 20 exactly, so you can reduce the fraction further to $^9\!/_{10}$. So instead of $^{180}\!/_{200} = {}^?\!/_{100}$, you would have $^9\!/_{10} = {}^?\!/_{100}$. Try solving this for practice. Did you get 90?

Math Buffs, Test Your Recognition Sensors!

Do you see a shortcut—a different way for solving the above problem?

Dottie needed $200. Dottie had $180. The fractional part of the money needed that Dottie had is $^{180}\!/_{200}$.

The fraction $^{180}\!/_{200}$ is the same as what percent? First change the fraction to a decimal equivalent. To find the decimal equivalent, we can simply divide

$$\begin{array}{r} .9 \\ 200\overline{)180.0} \\ \underline{180.0} \end{array}$$

Now let's turn this decimal into a percent. Do you remember how to change a decimal into a percent? Move the decimal point two places right and write %.

.9 = 90.% = 90%

Word Problems for Practice (XV)

Try solving these problems. Use the **percentage proportion** method first. Then **check** your answers with the **shortcut method**.

1. The worst team in the city basketball league was the Fourteenth Street Rippers. In a 20-game season, they ripped their way to a season of 1 win and 19 losses! What percent of games did they win? _____

2. During April, it rained often in Ravensville. It rained on 24 of the 30 days. What percent of the days in April did it rain? _____

3. Twenty high-school students signed up to take a Red Cross lifesaving course for swimmers. Fifteen of the students completed the course. What percent of the students completed the course? _____

4. Arlene and Alan liked to take walks in the woods to look for wildlife. On one walk, they counted 32 birds. Four of the birds were mockingbirds. What percent of the birds were mockingbirds? _____

(continued)

5. Gordon lived near a lake that was frozen much of the winter. One winter, Gordon made an ice boat that had large red sails and glided on the ice using metal runners. When the wind was brisk, Gordon could sail along the frozen lake. During that year, there were 13 weeks when the ice was solid enough for Gordon to use his ice boat on the lake. What percent of the weeks of that year could Gordon use his ice boat? (**Hint:** A year has 52 weeks.)

6. Ernestine had a spelling test at school. There were 40 words to spell. Ernestine got 32 of them right. What percent of the words did she spell correctly? _____

7. When Joan finished her computer training, she went to a high-tech job fair to look for a job. The fair was held at a big hotel for 3 days. 60 employers had booths at the fair, where they held interviews with people interested in finding jobs. If Joan had interviews with 9 of the employers, what percent of the employers did she talk with? _____

8. Denise was a very good dancer. She tried out for a part in a musical play in New York City. Fifty young people tried out for dancing roles in the play. The casting director chose five. What percent of the applicants were chosen? _____ Happily, Denise was one of those picked.

9. Mrs. Matlock assigned the students in her English class the task of writing a 1500-word composition on a current social issue. Trevor decided to write his paper on homeless families. Writing did not come easily for him, and after working on the paper a few hours, he found that he had written 300 words. What percent of the composition had he completed? _____

10. A scientist was teaching chimps to communicate by using a board covered with symbols. The chimps learned that each symbol referred to a real object around them or to some kind of action. For example, one symbol stood for "bananas." The scientist's goal was to teach the chimps the meanings of 150 of these different symbols. One chimp named Bernie learned 120 of the symbols. (a) What percent of the scientist's goal did Bernie achieve? _____ (b) Another chimp named Hercules only learned 45 of the symbols. What percent of the scientist's goal did Hercules achieve? _____

Type II Continued: More on Finding a Percent

In some problems that ask you to find a percent, the total is not given to you, but it can be calculated by adding up all the parts. For example, suppose you had this problem.

(continued)

Example	A baseball team won 30 games and lost 45. There were no ties. What percent of the games played did it win?
Solution	1. First find the total games played.

$$30 + 45 = 75.$$

2. The question asks, "What percent of the games played (75) did it win?"

3. You can now answer this question just as you did the other questions which asked you to find a percent.

(a) Write $^A/_B = {}^P/_{100}$

(b) P, you don't know. P is the ?.

B = 75 (the total)
A = 30 (the number which is compared with the total, because the question asks about **wins**)

$^A/_B = {}^P/_{100}$ becomes $^{30}/_{75} = {}^?/_{100}$.

So $75 \times ? = 3000$

DIVIDE

$$\begin{array}{r} 40 \\ 75 \overline{)3000} \\ \underline{300} \\ 0 \end{array}$$

The team won 40% of its games.

Word Problems for Practice (XVI)

1. The Girl Scouts collected $90 for charity while the Boy Scouts collected $60. What percent of the total amount was collected by the Girl Scouts?

   _____

2. In the first six months of the year, Bill made $1,000. In the second six months of the year, Bill made $3,000. What percent of this total did he earn in the first half of the year? _____

3. Jim, Florence and Mo bought an old beat-up car to drive to school. Jim gave $200 toward the purchase of the car, Florence $120, and Mo $80. What percent of the total did each pay?

   Jim _____ Florence _____ Mo _____

A Survey of the Graduating Class at Kennedy High School

The board of education was interested in the future plans of the graduating class at Kennedy High School. They passed out a questionnaire asking the students what they planned to do after having graduated. Here are the results:

120 students indicated that they planned to go to college.

50 students indicated that they planned to go to a school for technical training.

30 students indicated that they planned to find a job in the community.

20 students indicated that they planned to join one of the military services.

5 students indicated that they planned to travel.

25 students replied that they had no idea what they were going to do.

What percent of the students picked:

(a) College? _____

(b) Technical Training? _____

(c) Job in the Community? _____

(d) Military Service? _____

(e) Travel? _____

(f) Didn't Know? _____

Type III: Finding the Whole Amount

In the percentage proportion $\frac{A}{B} = \frac{P}{100}$, first we solved problems in which we were told what P (the percent) and B (the whole thing) were and we had to find A.

Next, we solved problems in which we were told what A and B were and we had to find P—the percent.

You may be wondering, are there problems where they tell us what A and P are and we have to find B—the whole thing? The answer is yes, indeed. Here is an example of such a problem.

Example	The high school drama club sold 50 tickets to its spring play. This was 25% of the total number of tickets it hoped to sell. How many tickets did the club hope to sell?
Solution	To solve this problem, write $\frac{A}{B} = \frac{P}{100}$. Then identify the letters:

P (the percent) is 25. Let's put 25 into the percentage proportion where P is. $\frac{A}{B} = \frac{25}{100}$

B is the total, the total number of tickets. We don't know the total; it is the missing part we are looking for. So B = ? Let's put ? into the percentage proportion where B is. $\frac{A}{?} = \frac{25}{100}$

A then is 50, the other number with which we are concerned, the number of tickets sold. It is the number that is compared with the total. Let's put 50 into the percentage proportion where A is.

$\frac{50}{?} = \frac{25}{100}$ or $\frac{50}{?} = \frac{1}{4}$ $1 \times ? = 200$ $? = 200$

If your recognition sensors are working and if you are "up on" fractions, you may have discovered another method for finding B, when B is the missing part in the percentage proportion.

(continued)

Let's look at this **other method** together. First, study the following question:

Example	Fifty percent of the students at Stoney Brook High School said they were in love. If 400 of the students at Stoney Brook said they were in love, how many students were there in the whole school? YOU ARE ASKED TO FIND THE TOTAL NUMBER OF STUDENTS IN THE WHOLE SCHOOL. THAT'S B.
Solution	Now think carefully about the problem. The number of students who said they were in love (400) is a fractional part (50% = $^{50}/_{100}$) of the whole student body at Stoney Brook. Or 400 is $^{50}/_{100}$ of what? Or 400 = $^{50}/_{100} \times$ what? Or 400 = $^{1}/_{2} \times$ what? You may remember from your study of whole numbers that when you want to find what multiplied by one number gives another, you should divide. In this problem, we want to find what multiplied by $^{1}/_{2}$ gives 400. To find the answer divide: $400 \div ^{1}/_{2} = 400 \times ^{1}/_{2} = 800$.

Word Problems for Practice (XVII)

Here are some problems for you to solve.

1. The Hudson family went fishing. They caught a lot of fish, but kept only 60% of what they caught. (The Hudsons threw the other fish they caught back into the lake because these fish were too small.) If the Hudsons kept only 12 of the fish they caught, what was the total number of fish they caught? _____

2. Yosef was looking through a collection of letters that had been written many years ago by a storekeeper who sold supplies to the Union Army during the Civil War. In this letter, the storekeeper complained that his income was being taxed at the rate of 3% per year to help pay for the war. If he paid $57 in income taxes that year, what was his income? _____

3. Gordon and Marissa were driving from Montreal to Washington, D.C. They had driven 388 kilometers and figured they had covered about 40% of the distance they would travel. About how long would their total journey be?

_____

(continued)

%

4. King Junior High School was starting a new library for its students. The school purchased 200 books. This was 25% of the number of books it planned to have. What was the number of books it planned to have?

    _____

5. Greg got a new battery for his portable radio. He played the radio for 15 hours. If this was 60% of the total time the battery would work, how many hours would the battery work? _____

6. Construction workers are repairing a section of highway. So far, they have repaired 2 kilometers of road. This is 40% of what they plan to do. How many kilometers of the road do they plan to repair? _____

7. Kevin put an electric drive on his bicycle. He charged the battery and then went riding. After riding 15 kilometers, he figured he had gone about 25 percent of the distance he could go without recharging. About how far would the bike go before needing a new charge? _____

8. A car manufacturer put out 3 new models: the Zippo, the Zappo, and the Zupper. The Zupper sold best, accounting for 60% of the total sales for the three cars. If sales for the Zupper totaled $6,000,000, what was the total sales for the three cars? _____

Word Problems That Deal with Increases and Decreases in Percents

This chapter introduces students to the concept of percent increases and decreases, especially in business. Starting with a description of a small business setting, involving charts of information, students are instructed about percent increases and decreases. Before practicing these problems, students are also introduced to growth rates in other areas. After practicing with word problems of this type, students are introduced to discounts and markups. Three styles of solution are given to solve these problems: the percentage proportion method, the fractional part method, and the markdown complement method. Students are then given word problems on which to choose their method and apply their knowledge. The final set of Word Problems for Practice in this chapter mixes up increase and decrease problems so that students can interpret problems and display their mastery of interpretive percentage problems.

Chapter 9 uses *Handy Rules* and specific examples to reach students who have already developed their calculation skills in percentages and are ready to apply them. The Word Problems for Practice in this section offer a wide variety of types of problems to ensure that students feel comfortable and confident with their interpretive percent problem solving.

Answers

Word Problems for Practice (XVIII)
1. 25%, **2.** 33.3%, **3.** 40%, **4.** 40%, **5.** 55%, **6.** 33.3%, **7.** 200%, **8.** 12%, **9.** 100%, **10.** 100%, **11.** 14%, **12.** 80%.

Word Problems for Practice (XIX)
1. $420, **2.** $9,800, **3.** $81.60, **4.** $300, **5.** $19.20, **6.** $25.25, **7.** $188, **8.** $360.

Word Problems for Practice (XX)
1. $10, **2.** $3.68, **3.** $18, **4.** $23.85, **5.** $2,592, **6.** $30,520, **7.** $26.

Word Problems for Practice (XXI)
1. a) 10, **b)** 50, **2.** 7,500, **3.** 1,950, **4.** 45, **5.** 1,248, **6. a)** 1,250, **b)** 3,750, **7.** 224, **8.** 20.

Word Problems That Deal with Increases and Decreases in Percents

In this chapter, we'll explain how to work problems that deal with increases or decreases in percents. Many of the problems will involve situations that you may run into in the world of business, either working for a business or dealing with a business as a consumer. So we'll use an example from business to start explaining just what we mean by "increases in percents" and "decreases in percents."

We could choose real examples from a big business, such as IBM or Exxon, but then the numbers we would have to deal with might be VERY BIG, so we have decided to start off with a very small business to make things easier for you. How small? Would you believe a lemonade stand?

Little Lucy Jones

Leroy Bixby Jones, the famous financial wizard, had a daughter named Lucy. As she was only ten years old and not very big, she was known as "Little Lucy." Lucy admired her father very much and wanted to start a career like his. Her father told her that he'd had his first success selling lemonade. So she decided to follow his footsteps. She had a sign printed that said,
"LITTLE LUCY'S LEMONADE"
The next day, she opened up a lemonade stand. In the beginning, business was slow. In the first month, Little Lucy only made $8.00. She thought the matter over and decided her business needed perking up. She tied some red and blue balloons to the lemonade stand and posted signs all around the neighborhood advertising her lemonade. Sales began to improve. For the second month, sales were $12.00.

"How's business going?" Bix asked his daughter.

"Okay, I guess," she replied. "I made 8 dollars the first month and 12 dollars the second month." Bix stroked his chin. "That's half again what you started with. That's an increase of 50 percent."

Lucy asked, "I know. Pretty good, isn't it?"

"Very good, Lucy. Very good."

The next month Lucy promoted her business even more. She gave out free bubble gum and baseball trading cards to kids who bought lots of lemonade. Sales climbed to $16. When Bix saw the figures, he smiled. "That's twice as much as where you started. You've gone from 8 to 16 dollars. That's an increase of 100 percent."

Lucy continued working hard to promote her business. Kids in the neighborhood could be seen wearing T-shirts with LUV LUCY'S LEMONADE written in big yellow letters. The business prospered. Soon, Lucy was making $24 a month, an increase of three times what she started with, or a 200 percent increase!

By the time Lucy closed down the stand in the fall, she was doing really good business, and her father was as pleased as punch.

(continued)

Little Lucy's Business Chart

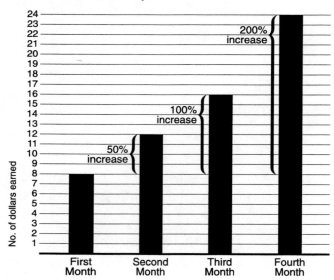

Rate of Increase or Decrease

Business problems about percents often include the phrases **rate of increase** or **rate of decrease**.

How do you figure the rate of increase or rate of decrease (if you're not so lucky)?

In the phrases **rate of increase** or **rate of decrease**, the word **rate** means **percent**. If you are asked to find the **rate of increase** or **rate of decrease**, you are really being asked to find **what percent** of the original amount the increase or decrease is. So, you must first find the increase or decrease. Let's say that like Little Lucy, you started with $8 and then made $12. Well, the first thing you notice is that you have an increase of $4.

$12   (The amount you ended up with)
–$8   (The amount you started with, or the original amount)
$4

To find the rate of increase, find what percent of **the original amount** ($8), the increase ($4) is.

Now you are ready to set up the percentage proportion. First, spell out what P, B, and A stand for:

P is the rate or percent. This is what you don't know or the ?.

B is the original amount ($8).

A is the increase ($4).

(continued)

The percentage proportion $\frac{A}{B} = \frac{P}{100}$ becomes $\frac{4}{8} = \frac{?}{100}$.

So, $8 \times ? = 4 \times 100$ or $8 \times ? = 400$

Divide 400 by 8, which gives 50.

This means that the rate of increase is 50%.

Let's try another example. Suppose you started with $8 and, like Little Lucy, ended up with $16. The increase is $8. If the percentage proportion is used to find the rate of increase,

P   =   ?

B   = $8

A   = $8

and we have $\frac{A}{B}$ = $\frac{P}{100}$ becoming $\frac{8}{8}$ = $\frac{?}{100}$

$8 \times ? = 800$

$800 \div 8 = 100$

The rate of increase is 100%.

Remember, that in using the percentage proportion to solve these problems, B is always what you started with, the original amount, and A is the change (increase or decrease).

Now, let's ask the question, what happens if you lose money? How do you calculate the percent of loss? Once again, to show you how to figure this out, let's use some small numbers.

Suppose you start with $50 and a month later you have only $30. You can see the actual loss is $20. ($50 – $30 = $20). Now, let's use the percentage proportion to figure out what percent this loss is of your original amount.

P = ?   (what we are looking for)
B = $50   (the original amount)
A = $20   (the amount of loss)

$\frac{A}{B} = \frac{P}{100}$ becomes $\frac{20}{50} = \frac{?}{100}$.

If we cross multiply, we get $50 \times ? = 2000$

$? = 40$ (Since your loss is 40% of what you had originally, we say your rate of decrease is 40%.)

Here is a different kind of situation where you might want to figure out the rate of decrease. Imagine, for example, that you were shopping and you saw some shoes on sale that had been reduced from $40 to $30. You want to know by what percent the shoes have been reduced.

To solve this problem, first find the decrease in cost: *(continued)*

$40 (original cost of the shoes)

−$30 (cost of the shoes during the sale)

$10 (the decrease in cost)

P is not known. So P is the ?.

B is $40 (original cost)

A is $10 (decrease in cost)

$\frac{A}{B} = \frac{P}{100}$ becomes $\frac{10}{40} = \frac{?}{100}$.

$40 \times ? = 1000$

The rate of decrease (or **discount rate**) is 25%.

25% is your savings!

Let's put what we have said into a small nutshell so that you will remember it very, very well.

A Handy Rule for Rates of Increase or Decrease

Rate of Increase and Rate of Decrease problems of all kinds—not just those involving money—can be solved by using the percentage proportion $\frac{A}{B} = \frac{P}{100}$.

In these problems: **P** is the rate or percent;

       B is the original amount;

       A is the increase or decrease.

Example	During the last two years, Northside High School put on a spring play. The first year, 400 people bought tickets to see the play. The second year, 600 people bought tickets to see the play. What was the percent increase in the number of people buying tickets from the first to the second year? _____
Solution	We can solve this problem the same way we solved the problem that asked about money.
	P is the percent. This is what we are looking for. P is the ?.
	B is the original amount (the number of people buying tickets the first year). This is 400.
	A is the increase (the difference between 600 and 400). $600 - 400 = 200$
	The percentage proportion $\frac{A}{B} = \frac{P}{100}$ becomes $\frac{200}{400} = \frac{?}{100}$
	$400 \times ? = 200 \times 100$
	$400 \times ? = 20,000$
	Divide 20,000 by 400 which gives 50.
	The answer is 50%.

Word Problems for Practice (XVIII)

1. They were having a "special" at Lyle's Auto Center. Usually, they charged $32 for a front wheel alignment and balancing of the tires. During the special, the charge for these services was $24. By what percent had the price been reduced? _____

2. Bess's church had a spring sale every year to raise money. The people brought things to the church they really didn't need. These items were sold at a big outdoor fair, with all the money going to the church. The first year they had the sale, they raised $1,800. The second year, they raised $2,400. By what percent did the money raised increase from the first year to the second year? _____ (Round to one decimal place.)

3. On Friday night, the Surfside Seafood House had an "All You Can Eat" seafood buffet for $20 per person. During the month of their tenth anniversary, they reduced the cost to $12. By what percent was the cost of the buffet reduced? _____

4. Mary Ann bought a cultured pearl necklace on sale. The original cost was $185. The new price was $111. What was the percent decrease in the price? _____

5. A club interested in wildlife was doing yearly counts of the number of snow geese that migrated to a marshland. The first year the club made the count, it counted 80 geese. The second year, it counted only 36 geese. What was the percent of decrease in the geese counted? _____

6. During one season, the Ludlow High School football team won the league championship by winning 12 games. The following season, the team won only 8 games. By what percent did its number of wins decrease? _____

7. A mad scientist named Dr. Masters drew up plans to build a tunnel under the Pacific Ocean between California and Japan. When asked how long it would take to build the tunnel, he replied, "Oh, two or three hundred years." He said he expected they would build only 3 kilometers of the tunnel the first year, but by the fifth year, they would be building 9 kilometers of tunnel. What percent increase would this be? _____

8. There was too much crime in Central City. The mayor decided to try a program of community policing—to get more police officers walking the streets of the neighborhoods. The program seemed to work. In the six months before the program started, there were 1,050 crimes reported. In the six months after the program started, there were 920 crimes reported. By what percent did the number of crimes decrease? _____ (Round your answer off to the nearest whole percent.)

(continued)

9. It seems like more and more young people are going to college. In 1980, in the graduating class of Lincoln High School, only 40 of the 400 graduates went on to college. This year, 80 of the 320 graduates are going to college. By what percent did the number of Lincoln High School graduates going to college increase between 1980 and the present year? _____ (This question is a little different than the others in this section; so be careful!)

10. AGL, Inc., a computer software development company, wanted to expand its workforce. The company had 45 employees and wanted to increase the number to 90. When the company completed its hiring, what would be the percent increase in the number of its employees? _____

11. The Kensington Junior High School library had a total of 250 books. A parents' group donated 35 new books to the library. What was the percent increase in the number of books in the library? _____

12. When the Green family went away for vacation, they boarded their pet dog, Rex, at the HHH Kennel. When Mr. Green found that the price for boarding Rex had gone from $10 a day last summer to $18 a day this summer, he muttered, "If the price goes up again next year, I'll stay here and Rex can drive!" What was the percent increase in the cost of boarding Rex at the kennel? _____

Calculating What the New Amount Will Be When the Original Amount Has Been Decreased or Increased by a Certain Percentage

Type I: Finding the New Cost After Markdown

DEBBIE'S
FASHION
SHOPPE

GOING OUT
OF BUSINESS
SALE
SAVE DOLLARS
DRESSES
COATS
PANTS SUITS
ALL 40%
OFF!
EVERYTHING
MUST GO!

Have you ever walked along a shopping mall or along a downtown street and seen a sign like this? The sign looks tempting. You may feel like dashing inside and buying everything in sight. It surely sounds like a bargain. But, maybe we should first figure out just what 40% off means. If something is marked 40% off, just how much is it going to cost in dollars and cents? We will now show you how to calculate this.

(continued)

Example	Suppose you want to buy a blue coat from Debbie's Fashion Shoppe. Last week, before Debbie's spring sale, it was marked $90. You wonder how much it costs now, at 40% off.
	We will now show you **several different ways** to find how much the coat now costs. All of these ways work!
Solution 1	**The Percentage Proportion Method**
	The first way which we will show you for solving the problem uses the percentage proportion.
	The cost now will be the ORIGINAL PRICE MINUS THE DECREASE IN COST. The **decrease in cost** is 40% of $90. What is 40% of $90? Let's use the percentage proportion to figure this out.
	P is 40 (the percent).
	B is 90 (the original amount).
	A is the amount of decrease (the part we don't know). A is the ?.
	So, $\frac{?}{90} = \frac{40}{100}$ $100 \times ? = 3600$
	If you divide 3600 by 100, you get 36. 40% of $90 is $36. That is the amount of the decrease or your savings. The **new cost** is the original cost **minus** the decrease which is $90 – $36 OR **$54**.
	The coat now costs $54.
Solution 2	**The Fractional Part Method**
	You can also find the decrease by thinking of the decrease as a fractional part of the whole. Many of you may want to use this method. Here is how you do it.
	The original price of the coat was $90. The new price is 40% off. Ask what is 40% of $90? Does that question ring a bell? When you are asked to find a fractional part **of** something, you can find the answer by **multiplying**.
	40% of $90 is the same as $\frac{40}{100} \times \$90 = \frac{3600}{100} = \$36$.
	40% of $90 is **also** the same as .40 × 90 = $36.00.
	Multiplying the percent of discount by the original amount gives you the amount of reduction in dollars and cents. If you subtract this figure ($36) from the original cost, you will have your new price ($90 - $36) = **$54**.
	Now you know two ways to find a new amount when the original amount has been decreased by a certain percentage.
	(Solution 3 follows on the next page.)

In either case, here is the rule to remember.

(continued)

A Handy Rule for Finding the New Cost After the Original Cost Has Been Marked Down

1. Find the **markdown** or **decrease in cost**.
2. Then subtract: THE ORIGINAL PRICE – THIS DECREASE.

Solution 3	**Markdown Complement Method**

Here is still another way of finding how much something costs after its price has been reduced by a certain percent. Many of you may find this method very easy to use.

Look at the same question, "A coat which originally sold for $90 is marked 40% off. What is the new price?" _____

The cost of the coat started at $90. Take where the coat started as 100%. Now 40% has been marked off the original cost. So, the new price is

100% – 40% or 60% of the original price.

60% of the original price is

$60\% \times \$90 = .60 \times \$90 = \$54.00$

(OR $^{60}/_{100} \times \$90$, if you prefer fractions)

Let's summarize what we have just done.

Another Handy Rule for Finding the New Cost After the Original Cost Has Been Marked Down

1. We subtracted the % of decrease from 100%.
2. We changed the percent we found in Step 1 into either a decimal or a fraction and multiplied that decimal or fraction by the original price.

Word Problems for Practice (XVIII)

Try these problems. You can do them by whatever method you feel most comfortable with.

1. If you bought a stereo set priced originally at $600, and it was 30% off, how much would it cost you? _____

2. If you bought a car at 20% discount (discount means markdown), and the original price was $12,250, how much would the car cost you? _____

3. Doris bought a tennis racquet that was usually priced at $96. She bought it during a sale when it was marked down 15%. How much did the tennis racquet cost her? _____

(continued)

4. Theo saw a guitar in the window of a music instrument shop. If the guitar usually sold for $500, but was specially priced at 40% off, what was the price of the guitar now? _____

5. Carmen went to a sale where she bought some cotton jeans at 20% off. The original price on the jeans was $24. What was the new price of the jeans? _____

6. Li bought a new leather handbag. The handbag was selling at 50% off an original price of $50.50. What was the cost of the handbag? _____

7. The Snowbound Ski Shoppe was selling skis regularly priced at $235 at 20% off. What was the new price of the skis? _____

8. Therisa was interested in learning how to film scenes for television. She saw an ad for a camcorder on sale. The camcorder, originally priced at $450, was listed at 20% off. What was the new price of the camcorder? _____

Type II: Finding the New Cost After Markup

Prices don't go down all the time, of course. Often, prices go up.

Example	Imagine that you have rented your first apartment. It is a nice little apartment that rents for $580 a month. One day, the landlord comes by and informs you that he has to raise the rent by 15%. What's it going to cost you now? _____
	We'll show you several ways to work a problem like this. The first way uses the percentage proportion.
Solution 1	**The Percentage Proportion Method**
	To solve problems like this, take your original amount, $580 a month. Add your increase of 15%. The new cost of rent will be the original cost plus your increase.
	Now how do we find what the increase of 15% is in dollars and cents?
	Ask what is 15% of $580? We can answer this using the percentage proportion.
	P is 15. B is $580 (the original amount). A is the ? (the amount of increase)
	The percentage proportion $^A/_B = {}^P/_{100}$ becomes $^?/_{\$580} = {}^{15}/_{100}$.
	$100 \times ? = \$8,700$
	Divide $8,700 by 100. You will get $87.
	The amount of increase is $87.
	The **new price** is the old price ($580) **plus** the increase ($87).
	$580 +$87 ‾‾‾‾‾ $667
	(Solutions 2 and 3 follow on the next page.)

(continued)

Solution 2   **The Fractional Part Method**

You can also find the increase by changing the percent to a fraction or decimal and multiplying.

The original amount of rent was $580. Ask yourself what is 15% of $580. You can find this by changing 15% to .15 and then multiplying.

$$\begin{array}{r} \$\,580 \\ \times\ .15 \\ \hline 2900 \\ 580 \\ \hline \$87.00 \end{array}$$

or you can change 15% to $\frac{15}{100}$ and multiply. Any way you do it, $\frac{15}{100} \times \$580 = \$87$.

The rent increase is $87.00. Add this increase to the original amount $580 and you will know what the **new rent** will be.

$580 + $87 = $667

 **A Handy Rule for Finding the New Amount After
the Original Amount Has Been Increased**

1. Find the increase.

2. Then add: ORIGINAL AMOUNT + THIS INCREASE.

Solution 3   **Markup Percentage Sum Method**

Now we'll show you a third method for working this kind of problem.

The apartment rents for $580 a month. The rent is increased by 15%. What's it going to cost you now?

Well, the rent started at $580. Take where the rent started as 100%. The rent has been increased by 15%. The new rent is 100% + 15% or 115% of $580.

115% of $580 is the same as 1.15 × $580 or $667.00

Word Problems for Practice (XX)

Here are some consumer problems that involve percent increases. To find the new costs, you may use the method you feel most comfortable with.

1. Andrew received an allowance from his father of $8 a week. On Andrew's birthday, his father increased Andrew's allowance by 25%. What was Andrew's allowance after his raise? _____

(continued)

      Word Problems with Decimals, Proportions, and Percents

2. The price of the supersize sundae at McPherson's ice-cream parlor (it had 4 scoops of ice cream, chocolate syrup, whipped cream and was covered with nuts and cherries) was $3.20. When Mr. McPherson raised the price of this bellybusting delight by 15%, what was the new price of the sundae?

   _____

3. Grace and Keisha opened up a dancing studio to teach the latest dances. When they started the studio, they charged $12 a lesson. After a while, they increased the price by 50%. What was the new price of a lesson? _____

4. Tran's mother paid $22.50 a month for her telephone bill. When the phone company announced an increase of 6% in the rate, how much would Tran's mother have to pay? _____

5. Tuition at the junior college was raised by 8%. If the price of tuition had been $2,400 a year, what would the new price of the tuition be?

   _____

6. There was a 9% increase in the salaries of teachers in the city's public schools. If a teacher had been making $28,000 a year, how much money would he be making after the raise? _____

7. The price of a hockey ticket at the Metropolitan Sports Arena was $25.00. After a 4% increase in ticket price, what was the new price? _____

Methods for finding a new amount after a percent increase or decrease can be used to solve many kinds of problems. Some of the problems may involve money, others may not.

Word Problems for Practice (XXI)

Here are some more problems for you to try. Remember to add increases and to subtract decreases.

1. A store began to sell a new line of unusual dolls that were dressed in costumes of different countries—countries in Africa, Asia, and Latin America. During the first month, the store sold 40 of the dolls. During the second month there was a 25% increase in sales.

   (a) What was the increase in the number of dolls sold? _____
   (b) How many dolls were sold the second month? _____

(continued)

2. Andrea wrote a mystery story and sent it away to a detective fiction magazine to see if the magazine would publish it. The story was 10,000 words long. The magazine editor said he liked the story, but asked her to reduce its length by 25%. How many words would the story have then? _____

3. Jackson Junior High School used to have 1,500 students. When Klegman Junior High School closed, some of its students were transferred to Jackson. The number of students at Jackson increased by 30%. How many students were now at Jackson? _____

4. Alison was running an experiment in chemistry class where she had to heat a mixture that included 30 grams of sulphur. The teacher told her to increase the amount of sulphur in the test tube by 50%. How many grams of sulphur would she then have in the test tube? _____

5. Last year, there were 1,560 auto accidents in Fairfield county. The police started cracking down on speeders. This year, traffic accidents were reduced by 20%. How many accidents were there this year? _____

6. During a period of bad times, it was very difficult for young people to find jobs. In one city, there were 5,000 teenagers looking for summer jobs. The city started up a youth employment program which found jobs for 25% of the young people.

7. How many of the young people found jobs? _____

8. How many of the young people were still looking for jobs? _____

9. If the navy of a certain country had 160 ships and it was decided to increase the number of ships by 40%, how many ships would there be after this increase? _____

10. A space scientist was making calculations for possible deep space probes to the outer planets of the solar system, Neptune and Pluto. He figured it would take him 1,000 hours to make these calculations, but with the aid of a high-speed computer, he cut the time down by 98%. How much time did it take him to make the calculations? _____

CHAPTER 10:

An Introduction to Calculating Interest

This chapter introduces students to the concept of calculating interest. Most students are familiar with the phrase "interest rates" from the television news, their local bank, or automobile sales ads. This chapter starts with a definition of interest and then introduces Simple Interest. There are several examples of simple interest displayed in a step-by-step process, and then students are given experience with similar problems. Next, compound interest is introduced. Again, a step-by-step example is given, as students learn about how interest is calculated in banks.

Chapter 10 uses *Handy Rules* and specific examples to reach students who have already developed their calculation skills in percentages and are ready to apply them. The Word Problems for Practice in this section offer practice with simple interest problems, and the chapter closes with a Brain Buster on compound interest.

Answers

Word Problems for Practice (XXII)

1. $3,600, **2.** $600, **3. a)** $20, **b)** $520,
4. a) $300, **b)** $5,300, **5. a)** $96, **b)** $896,
6. a) $64, **b)** $464, **7. a)** $15, **b)** $295,
8. a) $180, **b)** $2,580, **9.** $450, **10. a)** $2,160,
b) $12,160. **"Brain Buster!"** $2,201.41.

An Introduction to Calculating Interest

Now we'll discuss a very important use of percents. That use is in calculating **interest**. You may hear the word **interest** when you go to a bank, or you might hear it when you are buying a car or house. What is interest? Why do people have to pay interest?

Imagine for a moment that you are renting an apartment. The person who owns the apartment is loaning the use of the apartment to you. You have to pay for the use of the apartment. What you pay is called **rent**. You are paying a certain amount of money to the owner of the property to use something which has value.

Now money, of course, has value too. You can do a lot of different things with money: buy a car or house, take a vacation or pay for a college education. A lot of people want money for a lot of reasons. And when a lot of people want something, the item becomes valuable.

The companies that have lots of money— usually these are banks or finance companies— may let you use their money, but they will charge you for this use, just as the landlord will charge you for the use of his apartment. The charge for using money, however, is not called rent. It is called **interest**.

If you borrow money from a bank, you must pay the bank interest for the use of the money. On the other hand, if you put money into a bank in a savings account, you are loaning the bank money, and it will pay you interest, for the bank is going to use your money to make money for itself. So, interest can be a two-way street.

Let's begin by getting the meaning of some words very clear. The amount of money that is borrowed is called the **principal**. Suppose you want to borrow $6,000 to buy a car. That $6,000 you need is called the principal. Of course, you have to pay that back. The additional money we pay—the **interest**—is a fractional part of the amount we borrow. This fractional part is called the **rate**. The rate is expressed as a **percent**.

Interest can get to be a pretty difficult subject involving a lot of calculations. In this chapter, we'll be content to introduce you to two important kinds of interest: **simple interest** and **compound interest**.

Word Problems with Decimals, Proportions, and Percents

Name _____

Date _____

Simple Interest

A Handy Rule for Figuring Simple Interest

Interest = Principal × Rate × Time

Example	Leroy Bixby Jones, the financial wizard, once had to borrow money to run his business. Suppose Mr. Jones borrowed $1,000 at a **yearly** rate of 10% for **one year**. His interest would be:
	1,000 × 10% × 1.
Solution	However, we cannot multiply by percents. Before we can multiply, we must change 10% into **either** a decimal or a fraction. If we change 10% into .10, our arithmetic is as follows:
	$1,000 × .10 × 1 = $100.
	If we had changed 10% to $^{10}/_{100}$ = $^1/_{10}$ our arithmetic would have been:
	$1,000 × $^1/_{10}$ × 1 = $100.

Rule to Remember: If the rate is a YEARLY or ANNUAL rate, the time must also be expressed in years.

Example	If Mr. Jones had borrowed $1,000 at a **yearly** rate of 10% for 6 months, his interest would have been:
Solution	$1,000 × 10% × $^1/_2$ (6 months = $^1/_2$ year, since with a yearly rate, the time must be expressed in years)
	= $1,000 × $^1/_{10}$ × $^1/_2$
	= 100 × $^1/_2$
	= $50

(continued)

© 1982, 1999 J. Weston Walch, Publisher 107 *Word Problems with Decimals, Proportions, and Percents*

Name _____

Date _____

Example	Suppose Mr. Van Allen owed $300 on his credit-card account. If the *monthly rate* charged by his credit-card company were 16%, what would his interest be for 4 months? _____
Solution	Interest = Principal × Rate × Time

$$= \$300 \times {}^{16}\!/_{100} \times 4$$

$$= \$3 \times 16 \times 4$$

$$= \$48 \times 4$$

$$= \$192$$

Did you notice that when we had a **monthly** rate, we expressed our time in **months**?

Word Problems for Practice (XXII)

1. Find the interest on $10,000 at a yearly rate of 12% for 3 years. _____

2. Find the interest on $10,000 at a yearly rate of 12% for 6 months. _____

3. Mary Beth put $500 into a savings account at the city bank. Her money earned interest at a yearly rate of 4%. (a) If the bank paid simple interest, how much interest would her money earn in a year? _____ (b) At the end of a year, how much money would she have all together in the bank (principal plus interest)? _____

4. Mrs. Jamison put $5,000 into a special "certificate of deposit" at the bank that paid 6% interest per year. (a) If the bank paid simple interest on this money, how much interest would Mrs. Jamison earn in a year? _____ (b) How much money would she have in the bank at that point (principal plus interest)? _____

5. Syd bought a new stereo system. The equipment included a tuner, an amplifier, a tape deck, CD players, and speakers. The cost of the equipment was $800. Syd borrowed $800 from the bank at 12% interest per year for a period of one year. (a) How much interest did Syd pay the bank for the year? _____ (b) What was the total cost of the stereo system (price of stereo system plus interest)? _____

6. When Aaron's mother's washing machine broke down and flooded the basement, she decided that it was time to buy a new washing machine. She found a machine that she liked for $400. Being short of cash, she borrowed $400 from a bank that charged 8% simple interest. (a) If she borrowed this money for 2 years, how much interest did she pay the bank? _____ (b) How much did the washing machine cost her altogether (price of washing machine + interest?) _____

(continued)

© 1982, 1999 J. Weston Walch, Publisher   *Word Problems with Decimals, Proportions, and Percents*

7. Angela bought an automatic camera for $280. She paid $80 down and borrowed the remaining $200 from a finance company at 15% interest per year for a period of six months. (a) How much interest did she have to pay the finance company? _____ (b) How much did the camera cost her all together (price of camera plus interest)? _____

8. Leah was studying art at the university and wanted to take a trip to Europe where she could see many great paintings that she had read about. She figured the European trip would cost her $2,400. She had $1,200 and decided to borrow the remaining $1,200 from the University Credit Union. It charged her 10% interest per year. (a) If she paid the loan back in 1.5 years, how much interest would she pay? _____ (b) How much would the trip cost her in all? _____

9. LouAnne decided to go to college for 2 years. To help pay expenses, she borrowed $3,000 from a government-run student loan program. LouAnne was charged an interest rate of 7.5% per year. How much interest did LouAnne pay over the 2-year period? _____

10. The Alston family lived near a bay and everyone was interested in sailing. Mr. Alston decided to buy a sailboat. The boat cost $10,000. Mr. Alston paid $4,000 in cash and borrowed the remaining $6,000 from the bank. The bank charged him 12% interest per year. Mr. Alston paid the loan back over a 3-year period. (a) How much interest did he pay? _____ (b) How much did the boat cost him in all (price of the boat plus interest)? _____

Compound Interest

We have given you an introduction to the topic of interest. All of the problems we've asked you to solve have involved simple interest. The principal (the amount of money loaned or borrowed) stays the same over a certain period of time and interest is paid on that amount.

Now let's imagine that you open up a savings account with $1,000. After 3 months, the bank tells you that you have earned some interest, let's say $25. You could take out the $25 and spend it and still have your $1,000 in the bank. Or you could leave the $25 in the bank and have $1,025 in the bank; the principal has **grown**. It is now $1,025. In three more months, the bank will compute interest on that amount and your next interest check will be a little larger than $25, let's say $30. If you leave the $30 in the bank, your principal will grow further to $1,055, and your next interest check will be still larger. This is the basic idea of compound interest.

(continued)

So you can see that compounding interest increases both your principal and then your next interest payment. And the faster interest is compounded, the more you get of both. Some banks figure out interest every three months. Some figure it out every day. If interest is compounded every day, of course, you make more money than if it is compounded every three months, six months, or whenever.

If interest is compounded every day, it takes a lot of figuring. We wouldn't want to present a problem like that for you to try here. But just to close out this chapter, let's present one illustration so that you can see how compound interest is figured.

Example	Sally won $1,500 in a contest. She put the money into a savings account at the Southside Savings & Loan Association. Southside paid 6% interest per year and compounded the interest every 3 months. If Sally left her money in the bank for a full year, how much money would she have at that point?
Solution	Beginning deposit: $1,500 principal

Step 1.   Interest for the first three months:

$$\text{Interest} = \text{Principal} \times \text{Rate} \times \text{Time}$$
$$= \$1,500 \times 6\% \times {}^{3}\!/_{12}$$
$$= \$1,500 \times .06 \times {}^{1}\!/_{4}$$
$$= \$90 \times {}^{1}\!/_{4}$$
$$= \$22.50$$

Add interest to principal:

$$\text{New Principal} = \text{Last Principal} + \text{Interest}$$
$$= \$1,500 + \$22.50$$
$$= \$1,522.50 \text{ (Principal after 3 months)}$$

Step 2.   Interest for the second three months:

$$\text{Interest} = \text{Last Principal} \times \text{Rate} \times \text{Time}$$
$$= \$1,522.50 \times 6\% \times {}^{3}\!/_{12}$$
$$= \$1,522.50 \times .06 \times {}^{1}\!/_{4}$$
$$= \$91.35 \times {}^{1}\!/_{4}$$
$$= \$22.84$$

(Solution continued with Step 3 on the next page.)

(continued)

Add interest to the last principal:

New Principal = Last Principal + Interest

  = \$1,522.50 + \$22.84

  = \$1,545.34 (Principal after 6 months)

Step 3. Interest for the third three months:

Interest = Last Principal × Rate × Time

  = \$1,545.34 × 6% × $\frac{3}{12}$

  = \$1,545.34 × .06 × $\frac{1}{4}$

  = \$92.72 × $\frac{1}{4}$

  = \$23.18

Add interest to last principal:

New Principal = Last Principal + Interest

  = \$1,545.34 + \$23.18

  = \$1,568.52 (Principal after 9 months)

Step 4. Interest for the last three months:

Interest = Last Principal × Rate × Time

  = \$1,568.52 × 6% × $\frac{3}{12}$

  = \$1,568.52 × .06 × $\frac{1}{4}$

  = \$94.11 × $\frac{1}{4}$

  = \$23.53

Add interest to the last principal:

New Principal = Last Principal + Interest

  = \$1,568.52 + \$23.53

  = \$1,592.05 (That's how much Sally would have after a year.)

BRAIN BUSTER!

Joe deposited \$2,000 in the county bank at an interest rate of 6.5% for 18 months. His money was compounded every six months. How much money did he have in the bank at the end of the 18 months? _____

CHAPTER 11:

Solving Word Problems with the Aid of a Hand-held Calculator

This chapter introduces students to the use of a hand-held calculator in solving problems which require the use of decimals and a combination of steps to solve. The chapter starts with a discussion of the use of calculators and the need to interpret results as to whether they are reasonable. Next, there is a short description of the variety of technology available, and the minimum requirements of useful calculators. It is important for students to understand some of the limits of their tools, so the text walks them through three experiments to learn about their calculators: 1) the rounding capacities of the calculator, 2) what the calculator does when too many digits are required to display a small answer, and 3) what the calculator does when too many digits are required to display a large answer. With their understanding of their calculator enhanced, students are asked to work through several example problems which include decimal and percent calculations, done on the calculator, before tackling similar problems on their own.

Chapter 11 uses Solution Steps, student experimentation, and A Tip to Remember about calculators to build student confidence in using these powerful tools. This section only requires four-function calculators, the most basic type. The Word Problems for Practice in this section are a good chance for students to display their mastery of the concepts addressed elsewhere in these activities, as well as practicing calculator use. In this way, they build confidence in their mastery of interpretive multi-step problem solving.

Answers

Word Problems for Practice (XXIII)

1. 5.35 million voters, **2.** $43,121.45,
3. a) 2,257 calories, **b)** 2,539 calories, **4.** 15%,
5. $6.70.

The Percent Key

990 listeners.

Solving Word Problems with the Aid of a Hand-held Calculator

Sometimes the numbers used in solving word problems which occur in "real life" situations can be difficult to deal with and the calculations can take a lot of time, if we use only a paper and a pencil. However, the steps needed to solve these problems are the same steps we used earlier when the numbers were easy to work with. These steps are as follows:

1. Carefully examine the language of the problem—the key words, the phrases, and the ideas in the problem.
2. Determine the appropriate arithmetic operations used to solve the problem.
3. Perform the necessary calculations.
4. Ask whether or not the result makes sense.

A calculator may help you in the third step, which is performing the necessary calculations; but, remember—a calculator is only a tool. It cannot do Steps 2 and 4 which are listed above. A calculator is *not* a substitute for using your knowledge about mathematics.

We are just about ready to begin using our calculators. All you will need for our work is a very inexpensive 4-function calculator. You can recognize this type of calculator, because it has $+$, $-$, $\times$, $\div$, and $=$ keys.

In addition to having keys, all calculators have a display screen, which looks somewhat like a miniature TV screen. The number of digits that your calculator can display depends on the type of calculator you have. Your calculator may show 6, 8, 10, or 12 digits.

To learn something about your calculator, let's experiment. Turn your calculator on by pressing the "on" key. Now press 9 repeatedly. What do you see on your calculator's display screen? When we did this experiment on our calculator, we saw $\boxed{99999999}$.

This tells us a couple of things about our calculator:

1. We see eight 9's, so our calculator is an 8-digit calculator. Our calculator is limited, because it can display only 8 digits.
2. 99999999. or 99,999,999 is the largest number that our calculator can display.

Look again at what you saw on your calculator when you did this experiment. What did you learn about your calculator?

(continued)

Name _____

Date _____

If your calculator is not an 8-digit calculator, the results you get may sometimes be different from the results we get.

Now, look at the instruction booklet that came with your calculator to find out which key clears your calculator's display. Press your clear key, before doing our next experiments.

Experiment 1. To convert ⅔ into a decimal, press 2 ÷ 3 =

When we did this, our result was ⌐0.6666666¬. Notice that we have only 8 digits displayed, because our calculator is an 8-digit calculator. If we had divided 3)‾2‾ by hand, we would have gotten 0.666666666666666666 . . . and more 6's forever and ever! Our calculator chopped off the 6's when we reached more digits than our calculator could display. Other 8-digit calculators might have displayed 0.6666667, rounding the decimal off, instead of just chopping it off.

What did your calculator show when you did Experiment 1? Does your calculator round decimals off or does it simply chop them off, when it can display no more digits?

Experiment 2. Let's add 1,000,000 + 100.158.

To attempt this on our calculators, let's clear our calculators and then press

1000000 + 100.158 =

When we did this on our calculator, we got 1000100.1. However, if we add 1000000 + 100.158 by hand, we get 1000100.158. Our calculator chopped off the 5 and the 8. Why? Because in our earlier experiment, we learned that our calculator can display only 8 digits, and when it gets too many digits after the decimal point, it simply chops them off.

What did your calculator show when you did Experiment 2? Can you explain your result?

Experiment 3. Let's multiply 1,000,000 × 100.158.

To attempt this, clear your calculator. Always clear your calculator before beginning a new problem. Now let's press

1000000 × 100.158 =

When we did this on our calculator we got | 1.00158
error |

However, if we multiply 1,000,000 × 100.158 by hand, we get 100,158,000. When we first started discussing our calculator, we learned that the largest number it could display was 99,999,999. The correct product 100,158,000 was too big to be displayed; so, we had the error result on our calculator.

(continued)

114   *Word Problems with Decimals, Proportions, and Percents*

What did your calculator show when you did Experiment 3? Can you explain your result?

Much about mathematics in the "real world" deals with testing and then interpreting the results of the test. As we work with our calculators, we should always look very closely at our calculator results, and ask whether or not they make sense.

A TIP TO REMEMBER

A calculator is only a tool. Calculators can be useful; <u>but</u>, they have a problem representing many numbers, because calculators are limited in the number of digits they can display.

Now, let's try to use our calculators to calculate the answers to some word problems that deal with adding, subtracting, multiplying, and dividing decimals. A percent problem is also included. To make our task easier, we will use the same information in all four types of problems. The information will concern blood types.

In a survey, it was found that .42 of the people had Type A blood; .09 had Type B blood, and .03 had Type AB blood. The rest had Type O blood.

1. If there were 200 people in the survey, how many had Type A blood?

   _____

   Solution: .42 of the 200 people had Type A blood.

   So, to calculate the number of people who had Type A blood, we should multiply .42 × 200.

   To perform this calculation on our calculators, let's press .42 × 200 =

   Did you get 84 people?

   Can you calculate how many had Type B blood?

   .09 × 200 =

   Did you get 18 people?

   Can you calculate how many had Type AB blood?

   .03 × 200 =

   Did you get 6?

2. If all the other people in the survey had Type O blood, how many people had Type O blood? _____

   Solution: 84 had Type A. 18 had Type B. 6 had Type AB. If we add these numbers by pressing 84 + 18 + 6 =

(continued)

115   *Word Problems with Decimals, Proportions, and Percents*

we get 108. The rest of the 200 people had Type O blood. So, if we clear our calculators and then press 200 − 108 =

we see that 92 people in this survey had Type O blood.

3. What percent of the people in the survey had Type O blood? _____

Solution: Well, 92 people had Type O blood. 200 people were in the survey.

The fraction of the people who had Type O blood is $^{92}/_{200}$. Convert this fraction into a decimal by pressing 92 ÷ 200 =

Did you get 0.46? To convert a decimal to a percent, move the decimal point two places right and then write the percent symbol. If we do this, we see that 46% of the people had Type O blood.

Do the answers we got make sense? We can make a chart and use it to see that our answers make sense.

Blood Type	Number of People	Percent of People
A	84	42%
B	18	9%
AB	6	3%
O	92	46%

If we add the Number of People column, we get 200 people, the total number of the people in the survey. If we add the Percent of People column, we get 100%. From our earlier work, we know that 100% of the people make up the whole survey. So, this is another check which shows that our results make sense.

Word Problems for Practice (XXIII)

1. Only registered voters can vote in an election. In one state, 1.2 million people had registered as Democrats; 1.15 million had registered as Republicans; and 3 million had registered as Independents. How many people had registered to vote in this state? _____

2. A city's government was "in the red." It had spent more money than it had taken in. If it had spent $96,842.90 and had taken in only $53,721.45. what was the size of the city's debt? _____

3. A poster in the room where Joan took her dance class looked like this.

> **IF YOU DANCE, YOU WILL BURN**
>
> **12.54 CALORIES PER HOUR**
>
> **FOR EACH POUND OF YOUR WEIGHT**

(continued)

116   *Word Problems with Decimals, Proportions, and Percents*

Joan, who weighs 120 pounds, took Pete, who weighs 135 pounds, to her dance class. They danced 1.5 hours. Assuming that the poster information is accurate,

(a) How many calories did Joan burn? _____

(b) How many calories did Pete burn? _____

(**Hint:** In the questions (a) and (b) above, you must multiply three numbers.) Round your answers off to the nearest whole number.

4. In a survey of 5,000 college students, 750 said that they had sometimes dreamed in color. What percent of these students dreamed in color?

_____

5. The cost of electricity is found by multiplying three numbers.

number of kilowatts used in one hour × number of hours used × cost per kilowatt

Kelly's parents kept telling him, "Kelly, remember to turn off your light. Quit wasting electricity. It costs money."

Well, Kelly was a science buff; so, he decided to figure out what his parents were talking about. He said, "Let me figure out for myself what it would cost if I left my light bulb, which is marked 75 watts, on for 24 hours each day for each of the 31 days in July."

Kelly began by calling up the electric company. He asked, "How do I change watts into kilowatts?" They told him to divide his watts by 1,000. Kelly divided 75 ÷ 1000 = .075. His bulb used .075 kilowatt of electricity in one hour.

Next, Kelly figured out the number of hours there are in July. He thought, "24 hours each day for 31 days." Then, he multiplied 24 × 31 = 744, to find that he would use his light 744 hours during July.

From an old electric bill, Kelly noticed that the electric company charged $0.12 for each kilowatt hour.

Now, Kelly had all the numbers he needed. So, he multiplied

.075	×	744	×	.12 =
(kilowatts used each hour) × (number of hours used) × (cost per kilowatt)				

Use your calculator to help Kelly calculate the cost:

.075 × 744 × .12 = _____. Round your answer to two decimal places.

If you are interested, check the number of watts on your light bulb, find out what your electric company charges per kilowatt, and calculate the cost of keeping your bulb on for 31 days.

The Percent Key ÷

Your calculator may or may not have a percent key. If it doesn't, don't worry about it, because you really don't need a percent key. If your calculator does have a percent key, you may be curious about how to use it. In either case, let's look at an example which is related to a recent newspaper article.

Example	In a recent year, 78,000 American college students spent a year studying abroad, mainly in England or France. If 40% of them were in their junior year in college, how many of them were college juniors? _____
Solution	In our earlier work, we learned that we could solve a word problem like this by using the percentage proportion

$$\frac{A}{B} = \frac{P}{100}$$

Here P = 40; B = 78,000, and A = ? We also learned that we could find 40% of 78,000 by first changing 40% into .40 and then multiplying

$$78000 \times .40 = 31,200.$$

However, *if you have a % key, to find 40% of 78,000, you do not need to change 40% into .40 before multiplying.* You can simply press these keys on your calculator

$$78000 \times 40\%$$

and you will get 31,200. Regardless of which method you used, 31,200 students is the correct answer.

If you have a percent key, try this example.

Example	A radio station that broadcasts pop music did a survey of its listeners to find what kind of people were listening to their program. If they surveyed 1,650 people and found that 60% of the listeners were under the age of 18, how many of the listeners were in this group? _____